C000177835

Engineering and Construction Subcontract

This contract should be used for the appointment of a subcontractor for engineering and construction work where the contractor has been appointed under the NEC3 Engineering and Construction Contract

An NEC document

June 2005

NEC is a division of Thomas Telford Ltd, which is a wholly owned subsidiary of the Institution of Civil Engineers (ICE), the owner and developer of the NEC.

The NEC is a family of standard contracts, each of which has these characteristics:

- Its use stimulates good management of the relationship between the two parties to the contract and, hence, of the work included in the contract.
- It can be used in a wide variety of commercial situations, for a wide variety of types of work and in any location.
- It is a clear and simple document – using language and a structure which are straightforward and easily understood.

NEC3 Engineering and Construction Subcontract is one of the NEC family and is consistent with all other NEC3 documents.

ISBN (complete box set) 0 7277 3382 6
ISBN (this document) 0 7277 3368 0

Consultative edition 1991
First edition 1993
Second edition November 1995
Third edition June 2005

Cover photo, Golden Jubilee Bridge, courtesy of City of Westminster

9 8 7 6 5 4 3 2

British Library Cataloguing in Publication Data for this publication is available from the British Library.

Typeset by Academic + Technical, Bristol

Printed and bound in Great Britain by Bell & Bain Limited, Glasgow, UK

ONTENTS

ACKNOWLEDGEMENTS

The NEC first edition was produced by the Institution of Civil Engineer through its NEC Working Group.

The original NEC was designed and drafted by Dr Martin Barnes then Coopers and Lybrand with the assistance of Professor J. G. Perry then of t University of Birmingham, T. W. Weddell then of Travers Morgan Manageme T. H. Nicholson, Consultant to the Institution of Civil Engineers, A. Norm then of the University of Manchester Institute of Science and Technology a P. A. Baird, then Corporate Contracts Consultant, Eskom, South Africa.

The second edition of the NEC documents for engineering and constructi contracts were produced by the Institution of Civil Engineers through its N Panel.

The third edition of the NEC Engineering and Construction Subcontract w mainly drafted by Drick Vernon with the assistance of members of the N Panel.

The members of the NEC Panel are:

P. Higgins, BSc, CEng, FICE, FCIArb (Chairman)
P. A. Baird, BSc, CEng, FICE, M(SA)ICE, MAPM
M. Barnes, BSc(Eng), PhD, FREng, FICE, FCIOB, CCMI, ACIArb, MBCS, FInstCES, FAPM
A. J. Bates, FRICS, MInstCES
A. J. M. Blackler, BA, LLB(Cantab), MCIArb
P. T. Cousins, BEng(Tech), DipArb, CEng, MICE, MCIArb, MCMI
L. T. Eames, BSc, FRICS, FCIOB
F. Forward, BA(Hons), DipArch, MSc(Const Law), RIBA, FCIArb
Professor J. G. Perry, MEng, PhD, CEng, FICE, MAPM
N. C. Shaw, FCIPS, CEng, MIMechE
T. W. Weddell, BSc, CEng, DIC, FICE, FIStructE, ACIArb

NEC Consultant:

R. A. Gerrard, BSc(Hons), MRICS, FCIArb, FInstCES

Secretariat:

A. Cole, LLB, LLM, BL
J. M. Hawkins, BA(Hons), MSc
F. N. Vernon (Technical Adviser), BSc, CEng, MICE

The strategy for choosing the form of subcontract starts with a decision between five main Options, one of which must be chosen.

Option A	Priced subcontract with activity schedule
Option B	Priced subcontract with bill of quantities
Option C	Target subcontract with activity schedule
Option D	Target subcontract with bill of quantities
Option E	Cost reimbursable subcontract

One of the following dispute resolution Options must be selected to complete the chosen main Option.

Option W1	Dispute resolution procedure (used unless the United Kingdom Housing Grants, Construction and Regeneration Act 1996 applies).
Option W2	Dispute resolution procedure (used in the United Kingdom when the Housing Grants, Construction and Regeneration Act 1996 applies).

The following secondary Options should then be considered. It is not necessary to use any of them. Any combination other than those stated may be used.

Option X1	Price adjustment for inflation (used only with Options A, B, C and D)
Option X2	Changes in the law
Option X3	Multiple currencies (used only with Options A and B)
Option X4	Parent company guarantee
Option X5	Sectional Completion
Option X6	Bonus for early Completion
Option X7	Delay damages
Option X12	Partnering
Option X13	Performance bond
Option X14	Advanced payment to the *Subcontractor*
Option X15	Limitation of the *Subcontractor*'s liability for his design to reasonable skill and care
Option X16	Retention
Option X17	Low performance damages
Option X18	Limitation of liability
Option X20	Key Performance Indicators (not used with Option X12)

The following Options dealing with national legislation should be included if required.

Option Y(UK)2	The Housing Grants, Construction and Regeneration Act 1996
Option Y(UK)3	The Contracts (Rights of Third Parties) Act 1999
Option Z	*Additional conditions of subcontract*
Note	Options X8 to X11, X19 and Y(UK)1 are not used.

1

CORE CLAUSES

General

core
clauses

main
option clauses

secondary
option clauses

cost
components

subcontract
data

Actions 10

10.1 The *Contractor* and the *Subcontractor* shall act as stated in this subcontract and in a spirit of mutual trust and co-operation.

Identified and defined 11
terms

11.1 In these conditions of subcontract, terms identified in the Subcontract Data are in italics and defined terms have capital initials.

11.2 (1) The Accepted Programme is the programme identified in the Subcontract Data or is the latest programme accepted by the *Contractor*. The latest programme accepted by the *Contractor* supersedes previous Accepted Programmes.

(2) Completion is when the *Subcontractor* has

- done all the work which the Subcontract Works Information states he is to do by the Subcontract Completion Date and
- corrected notified Defects which would have prevented the *Employer* or the *Contractor* from using the *subcontract works* or Others from doing their work.

If the work which the *Subcontractor* is to do by the Subcontract Completion Date is not stated in the Subcontract Works Information, Completion is when the *Subcontractor* has done all the work necessary for the *Employer* or the *Contractor* to use the *subcontract works* or for Others to do their work.

(3) The Subcontract Completion Date is the *subcontract completion date* unless later changed in accordance with this subcontract.

(4) The Subcontract Date is the date when this subcontract came into existence.

(5) A Defect is

- a part of the *subcontract works* which is not in accordance with the Subcontract Works Information or
- a part of the *subcontract works* designed by the *Subcontractor* which is not in accordance with the applicable law or the *Subcontractor*'s design which the *Contractor* has accepted.

(6) The Defects Certificate is either a list of Defects that the *Contractor* has notified before the *defects date* which the *Subcontractor* has not corrected or, if there are no such Defects, a statement that there are none.

(7) Equipment is items provided by the *Subcontractor* and used by him to Provide the Subcontract Works and which the Subcontract Works Information does not require him to include in the *subcontract works*.

© copyright nec 2005   3

(8) The Fee is the sum of the amounts calculated by applying the *subsubcontracted fee percentage* to the Defined Cost of subsubcontracted work and *direct fee percentage* to the Defined Cost of other work.

(9) A Key Date is the date by which work is to meet the Condition stated. Key Date is the *key date* stated in the Subcontract Data and the Condit is the *condition* stated in the Subcontract Data unless later changed accordance with this subcontract.

(10) Others are people or organisations who are not the *Employer,* the *Proj Manager*, the *Supervisor*, the *Adjudicator*, the *Contractor, Subcontractor* or a employee, Subsubcontractor or supplier of the *Subcontractor*.

(11) The Parties are the *Contractor* and the *Subcontractor.*

(12) Plant and Materials are items intended to be included in the *subcontra works.*

(13) To Provide the Subcontract Works means to do the work necessary complete the *subcontract works* in accordance with this subcontract and incidental work, services and actions which this subcontract requires.

(14) The Risk Register is a register of the risks which are listed in t Subcontract Data and the risks which the *Contractor* or the *Subcontractor* h notified as an early warning matter. It includes a description of the risk anc description of the actions which are to be taken to avoid or reduce the risk.

(15) The Site is the area within the *boundaries of the site* and the volum above and below it which are affected by work included in this subcontract.

(16) Site Information is information which

- describes the Site and its surroundings and
- is in the documents which the Subcontract Data states it is in.

(17) A Subsubcontractor is a person or organisation who has a contract w the *Subcontractor* to

- construct or install part of the *subcontract works,*
- provide a service necessary to Provide the Subcontract Works or
- supply Plant and Materials which the person or organisation has who or partly designed specifically for the *subcontract works.*

(18) The Working Areas are those parts of the *subcontract working are* which are

- necessary for Providing the Subcontract Works and
- used only for work in this subcontract

unless later changed in accordance with this subcontract.

(19) Subcontract Works Information is information which either

- specifies and describes the *subcontract works* or
- states any constraints on how the *Subcontractor* Provides the Subcc tract Works

and is either

- in the documents which the Subcontract Data states it is in or
- in an instruction given in accordance with this subcontract.

Interpretation and the law **12**

12.1 In this subcontract, except where the context shows otherwise, words in the singular also mean in the plural and the other way round and words in the masculine also mean in the feminine and neuter.

12.2 This subcontract is governed by the *law of the subcontract.*

12.3 No change to this subcontract, unless provided by the *conditions of subcontract*, has effect unless it is has been agreed and confirmed in writing and signed by the Parties.

12.4 This subcontract is the entire agreement between the Parties

Communications **13**

13.1 Each instruction, certificate, submission, proposal, record, acceptance, notification, reply and other communication which this subcontract requires is communicated in a form which can be read, copied and recorded. Writing is in the *language of this subcontract.*

13.2 A communication has effect when it is received at the last address notified by the recipient for receiving communications or, if none is notified, at the address of the recipient stated in the Subcontract Data.

13.3 If this subcontract requires the *Contractor* or the *Subcontractor* to reply to a communication, unless otherwise stated in this subcontract, he replies within the *period for reply.*

13.4 The *Contractor* replies to a communication submitted or resubmitted to him by the *Subcontractor* for acceptance. If his reply is not acceptance, the *Contractor* states his reasons and the *Subcontractor* resubmits the communication within the *period for reply* taking account of these reasons. A reason for withholding acceptance is that more information is needed in order to assess the *Subcontractor*'s submission fully.

13.5 The *Contractor* may extend the *period for reply* to a communication if the *Contractor* and the *Subcontractor* agree to the extension before the reply is due. The *Contractor* notifies the *Subcontractor* of the extension which has been agreed.

13.6 The *Contractor* issues his certificates to the *Subcontractor*.

13.7 A notification which this subcontract requires is communicated separately from other communications.

13.8 The *Contractor* may withhold acceptance of a submission by the *Subcontractor*. Withholding acceptance for a reason stated in this subcontract is not a compensation event.

The *Contractor* **14**

14.1 The *Contractor*'s acceptance of a communication from the *Subcontractor* or of his work does not change the *Subcontractor*'s responsibility to Provide the Subcontract Works or his liability for his design.

14.2 The *Contractor*, after notifying the *Subcontractor*, may delegate any of his actions and may cancel any delegation. A reference to an action of the *Contractor* in this subcontract includes an action by his delegate.

14.3 The *Contractor* may give an instruction to the *Subcontractor* which changes the Subcontract Works Information or a Key Date.

Adding to the Working Areas **15**

15.1 The *Subcontractor* may submit a proposal for adding an area to the Working Areas to the *Contractor* for acceptance. A reason for not accepting is that the proposed area is either not necessary for Providing the Subcontract Works or used for work not in this subcontract.

core clauses

main option clauses

secondary option clauses

cost components

subcontract data

© copyright nec 2005 5

Early warning **16**

16.1 The *Subcontractor* and the *Contractor* give an early warning by notifying t other as soon as either becomes aware of any matter which could

- increase the total of the Prices,
- delay Completion,
- delay meeting a Key Date or
- impair the performance of the *subcontract works* in use.

The *Subcontractor* may give an early warning by notifying the *Contractor* any other matter which could increase his total cost. The *Contractor* ente early warning matters in the Risk Register. Early warning of a matter for whi a compensation event has previously been notified is not required.

16.2 Either the *Contractor* or the *Subcontractor* may instruct the other to attend risk reduction meeting. Each may instruct other people to attend if the oth agrees.

16.3 At a risk reduction meeting, those who attend co-operate in

- making and considering proposals for how the effect of the registere risks can be avoided or reduced,
- seeking solutions that will bring advantage to all those who will affected,
- deciding on the actions which will be taken and who, in accordance wi this subcontract, will take them and
- deciding which risks have now been avoided or have passed and can removed from the Risk Register.

16.4 The *Contractor* revises the Risk Register to record the decisions made at ea risk reduction meeting and issues the revised Risk Register to the *Subcontracte* If a decision needs a change to the Subcontract Works Information, the *Contra tor* instructs the change at the same time as he issues the revised Ri Register.

Ambiguities and **17**
inconsistencies

17.1 The *Contractor* or the *Subcontractor* notifies the other as soon as eith becomes aware of an ambiguity or inconsistency in or between the documen which are part of this subcontract. The *Contractor* gives an instruction res ving the ambiguity or inconsistency.

Illegal and impossible **18**
requirements

18.1 The *Subcontractor* notifies the *Contractor* as soon as he considers that th Subcontract Works Information requires him to do anything which is illegal impossible. If the *Contractor* agrees, he gives an instruction to change th Subcontract Works Information appropriately.

Prevention **19**

19.1 If an event occurs which

- stops the *Subcontractor* completing the *subcontract works* or
- stops the *Subcontractor* completing the *subcontract works* by the da shown on the Accepted Programme,

and which

- neither Party could prevent and
- an experienced subcontractor would have judged at the Subcontra Date to have such a small chance of occurring that it would have bee unreasonable for him to have allowed for it,

the *Contractor* gives an instruction to the *Subcontractor* stating how he is deal with the event.

The *Subcontractor*'s main responsibilities

Providing the Subcontract Works	**20**	
	20.1	The *Subcontractor* Provides the Subcontract Works in accordance with the Subcontract Works Information.
The *Subcontractor*'s design	**21**	
	21.1	The *Subcontractor* designs the parts of the *subcontract works* which the Subcontract Works Information states he is to design.
	21.2	The *Subcontractor* submits the particulars of his design as the Subcontract Works Information requires to the *Contractor* for acceptance. A reason for not accepting the *Subcontractor*'s design is that it does not comply with either the Subcontract Works Information or the applicable law.
		The *Subcontractor* does not proceed with the relevant work until the *Contractor* has accepted his design.
	21.3	The *Subcontractor* may submit his design for acceptance in parts if the design of each part can be assessed fully.
Using the *Subcontractor*'s design	**22**	
	22.1	The *Employer* and the *Contractor* may use and copy the *Subcontractor*'s design for any purpose connected with construction, use, alteration or demolition of the *subcontract works* unless otherwise stated in the Subcontract Works Information and for other purposes as stated in the Subcontract Works Information.
Design of Equipment	**23**	
	23.1	The *Subcontractor* submits particulars of the design of an item of Equipment to the *Contractor* for acceptance if the *Contractor* instructs him to. A reason for not accepting is that the design of the item will not allow the *Subcontractor* to Provide the Subcontract Works in accordance with

- the Subcontract Works Information,
- the *Subcontractor*'s design which the *Contractor* has accepted or
- the applicable law.

People	**24**	
	24.1	The *Subcontractor* either employs each key person named to do the job stated in the Subcontract Data or employs a replacement person who has been accepted by the *Contractor*. The *Subcontractor* submits the name, relevant qualifications and experience of a proposed replacement person to the *Contractor* for acceptance. A reason for not accepting the person is that his relevant qualifications and experience are not as good as those of the person who is to be replaced.
	24.2	The *Contractor* may, having stated his reasons, instruct the *Subcontractor* to remove an employee. The *Subcontractor* then arranges that, after one day, the employee has no further connection with the work included in this subcontract.
Working with the *Contractor* and Others	**25**	
	25.1	The *Subcontractor* co-operates with Others in obtaining and providing information which they need in connection with the *subcontract works*. He co-operates with Others and shares the Working Areas with them as stated in the Subcontract Works Information.

core clauses

main option clauses

secondary option clauses

cost components

subcontract data

25.2 The *Contractor* and the *Subcontractor* provide services and other things stated in the Subcontract Works Information. Any cost incurred by the *Contrac* as a result of the *Subcontractor* not providing the services and other things is to provide is assessed by the *Contractor* and paid by the *Subcontractor.*

25.3 If the *Contractor* decides that the work does not meet the Condition stated a Key Date by the date stated and, as a result, the *Contractor* inc additional cost either

- in carrying out work or
- by paying an additional amount to the *Employer* or Others in carrying work

on the same project, the additional cost the which *Contractor* has paid or incur is paid by the *Subcontractor*. The *Contractor* assesses the addition cost within four weeks of the date when the Condition for the Key Date is m The *Contractor*'s right to recover the additional cost is his only right in the circumstances.

Subsubcontracting 26

26.1 If the *Subcontractor* subsubcontracts work, he is responsible for Providi the Subcontract Works as if he had not subsubcontracted. This subcontra applies as if a Subsubcontractor's employees and equipment were t *Subcontractor*'s.

26.2 The *Subcontractor* submits the name of each proposed Subsubcontractor the *Contractor* for acceptance. A reason for not accepting the Su subcontractor is that his appointment will not allow the *Subcontractor* Provide the Subcontract Works. The *Subcontractor* does not appoint proposed Subsubcontractor until the *Contractor* has accepted him.

26.3 The *Subcontractor* submits the proposed conditions of contract for each su subcontract to the *Contractor* for acceptance unless

- an NEC contract is proposed or
- the *Contractor* has agreed that no submission is required.

The *Subcontractor* does not appoint a Subsubcontractor on the proposed su subcontract conditions submitted until the *Contractor* has accepted them. reason for not accepting them is that

- they will not allow the *Subcontractor* to Provide the Subcontract Works
- they do not include a statement that the parties to the subsubcontra shall act in a spirit of mutual trust and co-operation.

Other responsibilities 27

27.1 The *Subcontractor* obtains approval of his design from Others where necessar

27.2 The *Subcontractor* provides access to work being done and to Plant a Materials being stored for this subcontract for

- the *Contractor,*
- the *Project Manager,*
- the *Supervisor* and
- Others notified to him by the *Contractor* or the *Project Manager.*

27.3 The *Subcontractor* obeys an instruction which is in accordance with this su contract and is given to him by the *Contractor*.

27.4 The *Subcontractor* acts in accordance with the health and safety requiremen stated in the Subcontract Works Information.

Time

Starting, Completion and Key Dates	**30**

30.1 The *Subcontractor* does not start work on the Site until the first *subcontract access date* and does the work so that Completion is on or before the Subcontract Completion Date.

30.2 The *Contractor* decides the date of Completion. The *Contractor* certifies Completion within one week of Completion.

30.3 The *Subcontractor* does the work so that the Condition stated for each Key Date is met by the Key Date.

The programme **31**

31.1 If a programme is not identified in the Subcontract Data, the *Subcontractor* submits a first programme to the *Contractor* for acceptance within the period stated in the Subcontract Data.

31.2 The *Subcontractor* shows on each programme which he submits for acceptance

- the *subcontract starting date, subcontract access dates,* Key Dates and Subcontract Completion Date,
- planned Completion,
- the order and timing of the operations which the *Subcontractor* plans to do in order to Provide the Subcontract Works,
- the order and timing of the work of the *Employer,* the *Contractor* and Others as last agreed with them by the *Subcontractor* or, if not so agreed, as stated in the Subcontract Works Information,
- the dates when the *Subcontractor* plans to meet each Condition stated for the Key Dates and to complete other work needed to allow the *Employer,* the *Contractor* and Others to do their work,
- provisions for

  - float,
  - time risk allowances,
  - health and safety requirements and
  - the procedures set out in this subcontract,

- the dates when, in order to Provide the Subcontract Works in accordance with his programme, the *Subcontractor* will need

  - access to a part of the Site if later than its *subcontract access date,*
  - acceptances,
  - Plant and Materials and other things to be provided by the *Employer* and the *Contractor* and
  - information from Others,

- for each operation, a statement of how the *Subcontractor* plans to do the work identifying the principal Equipment and other resources which he plans to use and
- other information which the Subcontract Works Information requires the *Subcontractor* to show on a programme submitted for acceptance.

31.3 Within two weeks of the *Subcontractor* submitting a programme to him for acceptance, the *Contractor* either accepts the programme or notifies the *Subcontractor* of his reasons for not accepting it. A reason for not accepting a programme is that

- the *Subcontractor*'s plans which it shows are not practicable,
- it does not show the information which this subcontract requires,
- it does not represent the *Subcontractor*'s plans realistically or
- it does not comply with the Subcontract Works Information.

Revising the programme **32**

32.1   The *Subcontractor* shows on each revised programme

- the actual progress achieved on each operation and its effect upon t timing of the remaining work,
- the effects of implemented compensation events and of notified ea warning matters,
- how the *Subcontractor* plans to deal with any delays and to corre notified Defects and
- any other changes which the *Subcontractor* proposes to make to t Accepted Programme.

32.2   The *Subcontractor* submits a revised programme to the *Contractor* f acceptance

- within the *period for reply* after the *Contractor* has instructed him to,
- when the *Subcontractor* chooses to and, in any case,
- at no longer interval than the interval stated in the Subcontract Da from the *subcontract starting date* until Completion of the whole of t *subcontract works*.

Access to and use of **33**
the Site 33.1   The *Contractor* allows access to and use of each part of the Site to t *Subcontractor* which is necessary for the work included in this subcontra Access and use is allowed on or before the later of its *subcontract acce date* and the date for access shown on the Accepted Programme.

Instructions to stop or not **34**
to start work 34.1   The *Contractor* may instruct the *Subcontractor* to stop or not to start any wo and may later instruct him that he may re-start or start it.

Take over **35**

35.1   The *Contractor* need not take over the *subcontract works* before the Su contract Completion Date if it is stated in the Subcontract Data that he is n willing to do so. Otherwise the *Contractor* takes over the *subcontract works* n later than two weeks after Completion.

35.2   The *Employer* or the *Contractor* may use any part of the *subcontract wor* before Completion has been certified. If he does so, the *Contractor* takes ov the part of the *subcontract works* when the *Employer* or the *Contractor* begin to use it except if the use is

- for a reason stated in the Subcontract Works Information or
- to suit the *Subcontractor*'s method of working.

35.3   The *Contractor* certifies the date upon which he takes over any part of th *subcontract works* and its extent within two weeks of the date.

Acceleration **36**

36.1   The *Contractor* may instruct the *Subcontractor* to submit a quotation for a acceleration to achieve Completion before the Subcontract Completion Dat The *Contractor* states changes to the Key Dates to be included in th quotation. A quotation for an acceleration comprises proposed changes to th Prices and a revised programme showing the earlier Subcontract Completic Date and the changed Key Dates. The *Subcontractor* submits details of h assessment with each quotation.

36.2   The *Subcontractor* submits a quotation or gives his reasons for not doing s within the *period for reply*.

Testing and Defects

Tests and inspections **40**

40.1 The subclauses in this clause only apply to tests and inspections required by the Subcontract Works Information or the applicable law.

40.2 The *Subcontractor,* the *Contractor* and the *Employer* provide materials, facilities and samples for tests and inspections as stated in the Subcontract Works Information.

40.3 The *Subcontractor* and the *Contractor* each notifies the other of each of his tests and inspections before it starts and afterwards notifies the other of its results. The *Subcontractor* notifies the *Contractor* in time for a test or inspection to be arranged and done before doing work which would obstruct the test or inspection. The *Contractor* and the *Supervisor* may watch any test done by the *Subcontractor.*

40.4 If a test or inspection shows that any work has a Defect, the *Subcontractor* corrects the Defect and the test or inspection is repeated.

40.5 The *Contractor* does his tests and inspections without causing unnecessary delay to the work or to a payment which is conditional upon a test or inspection being successful. A payment which is conditional upon a *Contractor*'s or *Supervisor*'s test or inspection being successful becomes due at the later of the *defects date* and the end of the last *defect correction period* if

- the *Contractor* or the *Supervisor* has not done the test or inspection and
- the delay to the test or inspection is not the *Subcontractor*'s fault.

40.6 The *Contractor* assesses the cost incurred by him in repeating a test or inspection after a Defect is found. The *Subcontractor* pays the amount assessed.

Testing and inspection **41**
before delivery 41.1 The *Subcontractor* does not bring to the Working Areas those Plant and Materials which the Subcontract Works Information states are to be tested or inspected before delivery until the *Contractor* has notified the *Subcontractor* that they have passed the test or inspection.

Searching for and notifying **42**
Defects 42.1 Until the *defects date*, the *Contractor* may instruct the *Subcontractor* to search for a Defect. He gives his reason for the search with his instruction. Searching may include

- uncovering, dismantling, re-covering and re-erecting work,
- providing facilities, materials and samples for tests and inspections done by the *Contractor* or the *Supervisor* and
- doing tests and inspections which the Subcontract Works Information does not require.

42.2 Until the *defects date*, the *Contractor* promptly notifies the *Subcontractor* of each Defect as soon as he finds it and the *Subcontractor* promptly notifies the *Contractor* of each Defect as soon as he finds it.

Correcting Defects **43**

43.1 The *Subcontractor* corrects a Defect whether or not the *Contractor* notifies him of it.

43.2 The *Subcontractor* corrects a notified Defect before the end of the *defect correction period*. The *defect correction period* begins at Completion for Defects notified before Completion and when the Defect is notified for other Defects.

core clauses

main option clauses

secondary option clauses

cost components

subcontract data

43.3 The *Contractor* issues the Defects Certificate at the later of the *defects da* and the end of the last *defect correction period*. The *Employer*'s or the *Cor tractor*'s rights in respect of a Defect which the *Contractor* has not found « notified are not affected by the issue of the Defects Certificate.

43.4 The *Contractor* arranges for the *Employer* and the *Contractor* to allow th *Subcontractor* access to and use of a part of the *subcontract works* which th *Contractor* has taken over if they are needed for correcting a Defect. In th case the *defect correction period* begins when the necessary access and us have been provided.

Accepting Defects 44

44.1 The *Subcontractor* and the *Contractor* may each propose to the other that th Subcontract Works Information should be changed so that a Defect does n« have to be corrected.

44.2 If the *Subcontractor* and the *Contractor* are prepared to consider the chang« the *Subcontractor* submits a quotation for reduced Prices or an earli« Subcontract Completion Date or both to the *Contractor* for acceptance. If th *Contractor* accepts the quotation, he gives an instruction to change th Subcontract Works Information, the Prices and the Subcontract Completio Date accordingly.

Uncorrected Defects 45

45.1 If the *Subcontractor* is given access in order to correct a notified Defect but h has not corrected it within its *defect correction period*, the *Contract«* assesses the cost to him of having the Defect corrected by other people an the *Subcontractor* pays this amount. The Subcontract Works Information i treated as having been changed to accept the Defect.

45.2 If the *Subcontractor* is not given access in order to correct a notified Defe« before the *defects date*, the *Contractor* assesses the cost to the *Subcontract«* of correcting the Defect and the *Subcontractor* pays this amount. Th Subcontract Works Information is treated as having been changed to acce| the Defect.

 www.neccontract.co■

Payment

assessing the amount due 50

50.1 The *Contractor* assesses the amount due at each assessment date. The first assessment date is decided by the *Contractor* to suit the procedures of the Parties and is not later than the *assessment interval* after the *subcontract starting date*. Later assessment dates occur

- at the end of each *assessment interval* until four weeks after the *Contractor* issues the Defects Certificate and
- at Completion of the whole of the *subcontract works*.

50.2 The amount due is

- the Price for Work Done to Date,
- plus other amounts to be paid to the *Subcontractor*,
- less amounts to be paid by or retained from the *Subcontractor*.

Any tax which the law requires the *Contractor* to pay to the *Subcontractor* is included in the amount due.

50.3 If no programme is identified in the Subcontract Data, one quarter of the Price for Work Done to Date is retained in assessments of the amount due until the *Subcontractor* has submitted a first programme to the *Contractor* for acceptance showing the information which this subcontract requires.

50.4 In assessing the amount due, the *Contractor* considers any application for payment the *Subcontractor* has submitted on or before the assessment date. The *Contractor* gives the *Subcontractor* details of how the amount due has been assessed.

50.5 The *Contractor* corrects any wrongly assessed amount due in a later payment certificate.

Payment 51

51.1 The *Contractor* certifies a payment within two weeks of each assessment date. The first payment is the amount due. Other payments are the change in the amount due since the last payment certificate. A payment is made by the *Subcontractor* to the *Contractor* if the change reduces the amount due. Other payments are made by the *Contractor* to the *Subcontractor*. Payments are in the *currency of this subcontract* unless otherwise stated in this subcontract.

51.2 Each certified payment is made within four weeks of the assessment date or, if a different period is stated in the Subcontract Data, within the period stated. If a certified payment is late, or if a payment is late because the *Contractor* does not issue a certificate which he should issue, interest is paid on the late payment. Interest is assessed from the date by which the late payment should have been made until the date when the late payment is made, and is included in the first assessment after the late payment is made.

51.3 If an amount due is corrected in a later certificate either

- by the *Contractor* in relation to a mistake or a compensation event or
- following a decision of the *Adjudicator* or the *tribunal*,

interest on the correcting amount is paid. Interest is assessed from the date when the incorrect amount was certified until the date when the correcting amount is certified and is included in the assessment which includes the correcting amount.

51.4 Interest is calculated on a daily basis at the *interest rate* and is compounded annually.

core clauses

main option clauses

secondary option clauses

cost components

subcontract data

Defined Cost 52

52.1 All the *Subcontractor*'s costs which are not included in the Defined Cost are treated as included in the Fee. Defined Cost includes only amounts calculated using rates and percentages stated in the Subcontract Data and other amounts at open market or competitively tendered prices with deductions for all discounts, rebates and taxes which can be recovered.

6 Compensation events

Compensation events 60

60.1 The following are compensation events.

(1) The *Contractor* gives an instruction changing the Subcontract Works Information except

- a change made in order to accept a Defect or
- a change to the Subcontract Works Information provided by the *Subcontractor* for his design which is made either at his request or to comply with other Subcontract Works Information provided by the *Contractor*.

(2) The *Contractor* does not allow access to and use of a part of the Site by the later of its *subcontract access date* and the date shown on the Accepted Programme.

(3) The *Contractor* does not provide something which he is to provide by the date for providing it shown on the Accepted Programme.

(4) The *Contractor* gives an instruction to stop or not to start any work or to change a Key Date.

(5) The *Employer,* the *Contractor* or Others

- do not work within the times shown on the Accepted Programme,
- do not work within the conditions stated in the Subcontract Works Information or
- carry out work on the Site that is not stated in the Subcontract Works Information.

(6) The *Contractor* does not reply to a communication from the *Subcontractor* within the period required by this subcontract.

(7) The *Contractor* gives an instruction for dealing with an object of value or of historical or other interest found within the Site.

(8) The *Contractor* changes a decision which he has previously communicated to the *Subcontractor.*

(9) The *Contractor* withholds an acceptance (other than acceptance of a quotation for acceleration or for not correcting a Defect) for a reason not stated in this subcontract.

(10) The *Contractor* instructs the *Subcontractor* to search for a Defect and no Defect is found unless the search is needed only because the *Subcontractor* gave insufficient notice of doing work obstructing a required test or inspection.

(11) A test or inspection done by the *Contractor* or the *Supervisor* causes unnecessary delay.

(12) The *Subcontractor* encounters physical conditions which

- are within the Site,
- are not weather conditions and
- an experienced subcontractor would have judged at the Subcontract Date to have such a small chance of occurring that it would have been unreasonable for him to have allowed for them.

Only the difference between the physical conditions encountered and those for which it would have been reasonable to have allowed is taken into account in assessing a compensation event.

core clauses

main option clauses

secondary option clauses

cost components

subcontract data

(13) A *weather measurement* is recorded

- within a calendar month,
- before the Subcontract Completion Date for the whole of the *subcontract works* and
- at the place stated in the Subcontract Data

the value of which, by comparison with the *weather data*, is shown to occur on average less frequently than once in ten years.

Only the difference between the *weather measurement* and the weather which the *weather data* show to occur on average less frequently than once in ten years is taken into account in assessing a compensation event.

(14) An event which is an *Employer*'s or a *Contractor*'s risk stated in this subcontract.

(15) The *Contractor* certifies take over of a part of the *subcontract works* before both Completion and the Subcontract Completion Date.

(16) The *Contractor* or the *Employer* does not provide materials, facilities and samples for tests and inspections as stated in the Subcontract Works Information.

(17) The *Contractor* notifies a correction to an assumption which he has stated about a compensation event.

(18) A breach of subcontract by the *Contractor* which is not one of the other compensation events in this subcontract.

(19) An event which

- stops the *Subcontractor* completing the *subcontract works* or
- stops the *Subcontractor* completing the *subcontract works* by the date shown on the Accepted Programme,

and which

- neither Party could prevent,
- an experienced subcontractor would have judged at the Subcontract Date to have such a small chance of occurring that it would have been unreasonable for him to have allowed for it and
- is not one of the other compensation events stated in this subcontract.

60.2 In judging the physical conditions for the purpose of assessing a compensation event, the *Subcontractor* is assumed to have taken into account

- the Site Information,
- publicly available information referred to in the Site Information,
- information obtainable from a visual inspection of the Site and
- other information which an experienced subcontractor could reasonably be expected to have or to obtain.

60.3 If there is an ambiguity or inconsistency within the Site Information (including the information referred to in it), the *Subcontractor* is assumed to have taken into account the physical conditions more favourable to doing the work.

Notifying compensation events **61**

61.1 For compensation events which arise from the *Contractor* giving an instruction or changing an earlier decision, the *Contractor* notifies the *Subcontractor* of the compensation event at the time of giving the instruction or changing the earlier decision. He also instructs the *Subcontractor* to submit quotations unless the event arises from a fault of the *Subcontractor* or quotations have already been submitted. The *Subcontractor* puts the instruction or changed decision into effect.

61.2 The *Contractor* may instruct the *Subcontractor* to submit quotations for a proposed instruction or a proposed changed decision. The *Subcontractor* does not put a proposed instruction or a proposed changed decision into effect.

61.3 The *Subcontractor* notifies the *Contractor* of an event which has happened or which he expects to happen as a compensation event if

- the *Subcontractor* believes that the event is a compensation event and
- the *Contractor* has not notified the event to the *Subcontractor*.

If the *Subcontractor* does not notify a compensation event within seven weeks of becoming aware of the event, he is not entitled to a change in the Prices, the Subcontract Completion Date or a Key Date unless the *Contractor* should have notified the event to the *Subcontractor* but did not.

61.4 If the *Contractor* decides that an event notified by the *Subcontractor*

- arises from a fault of the *Subcontractor*,
- has not happened and is not expected to happen,
- has no effect upon Defined Cost, Completion or meeting a Key Date or
- is not one of the compensation events stated in this subcontract

he notifies the *Subcontractor* of his decision that the Prices, the Completion Date and Key Dates are not to be changed.

If the *Contractor* decides otherwise, he notifies the *Subcontractor* accordingly and instructs him to submit quotations.

If the *Contractor* does not notify his decision to the *Subcontractor* within either

- two weeks of the *Subcontractor*'s notification or
- a longer period to which the *Subcontractor* has agreed,

the *Subcontractor* may notify the *Contractor* to this effect. A failure by the *Contractor* to reply within three weeks of this notification is treated as acceptance by the *Contractor* that the event is a compensation event and an instruction to submit quotations.

61.5 If the *Contractor* decides that the *Subcontractor* did not give an early warning of the event which an experienced subcontractor could have given, he notifies this decision to the *Subcontractor* when he instructs him to submit quotations.

61.6 If the *Contractor* decides that the effects of a compensation event are too uncertain to be forecast reasonably, he states assumptions about the nature of the event in his instruction to the *Subcontractor* to submit quotations. Assessment of the event is based on these assumptions. If any of them is later found to have been wrong, the *Contractor* notifies a correction.

61.7 A compensation event is not notified after the *defects date*.

Quotations for **62**
compensation events 62.1 After discussing with the *Subcontractor* different ways of dealing with the compensation event which are practicable, the *Contractor* may instruct the *Subcontractor* to submit alternative quotations. The *Subcontractor* submits the required quotations to the *Contractor* and may submit quotations for other methods of dealing with the compensation event which he considers practicable.

62.2 Quotations for compensation events comprise proposed changes to the Prices and any delay to the Subcontract Completion Date and Key Dates assessed by the *Subcontractor*. The *Subcontractor* submits details of his assessment with each quotation. If the programme for remaining work is altered by the compensation event, the *Subcontractor* includes the alterations to the Accepted Programme in his quotation.

62.3 The *Subcontractor* submits quotations within one week of being instructed to do so by the *Contractor.* The *Contractor* replies within four weeks of the submission. His reply is

- an instruction to submit a revised quotation,
- an acceptance of a quotation,
- a notification that a proposed instruction will not be given or a proposed changed decision will not be made or
- a notification that he will be making his own assessment.

62.4 The *Contractor* instructs the *Subcontractor* to submit a revised quotation only after explaining his reasons for doing so to the *Subcontractor*. The *Subcontractor* submits the revised quotation within one week of being instructed to do so.

62.5 The *Contractor* extends the time allowed for

- the *Subcontractor* to submit quotations for a compensation event and
- the *Contractor* to reply to a quotation

if the *Contractor* and the *Subcontractor* agree to the extension before the submission or reply is due. The *Contractor* notifies the extension that has been agreed to the *Subcontractor*.

62.6 If the *Contractor* does not reply to a quotation within the time allowed, the *Subcontractor* may notify the *Contractor* to this effect. If the *Subcontractor* submitted more than one quotation for the compensation event, he states in his notification which quotation he proposes is to be accepted. If the *Contractor* does not reply to the notification within three weeks, and unless the quotation is for a proposed instruction or a proposed changed decision, the *Subcontractor*'s notification is treated as acceptance of the quotation by the *Contractor*.

Assessing compensation events 63

63.1 The changes to the Prices are assessed as the effect of the compensation event upon

- the actual Defined Cost of the work already done,
- the forecast Defined Cost of the work not yet done and
- the resulting Fee.

The date when the *Contractor* instructed or should have instructed the *Subcontractor* to submit quotations divides the work already done from the work not yet done.

63.2 If the effect of a compensation event is to reduce the total Defined Cost, the Prices are not reduced except as stated in this subcontract.

63.3 A delay to the Subcontract Completion Date is assessed as the length of time that, due to the compensation event, planned Completion is later than planned Completion as shown on the Accepted Programme. A delay to a Key Date is assessed as the length of time that, due to the compensation event, the planned date when the Condition stated for a Key Date will be met is later than the date shown on the Accepted Programme.

63.4 The rights of the *Contractor* and the *Subcontractor* to changes to the Prices, the Subcontract Completion Date and the Key Dates are their only rights in respect of a compensation event.

63.5 If the *Contractor* has notified the *Subcontractor* of his decision that the *Subcontractor* did not give an early warning of a compensation event which an experienced subcontractor could have given, the event is assessed as if the *Subcontractor* had given early warning.

63.6 Assessment of the effect of a compensation event includes risk allowances for cost and time for matters which have a significant chance of occurring and are at the *Subcontractor*'s risk under this subcontract.

63.7 Assessments are based upon the assumptions that the *Subcontractor* reacts competently and promptly to the compensation event, that any Defined Cost and time due to the event are reasonably incurred and that the Accepted Programme can be changed.

63.8 A compensation event which is an instruction to change the Subcontract Works Information in order to resolve an ambiguity or inconsistency is assessed as if the Prices, the Subcontract Completion Date and the Key Dates were for the interpretation most favourable to the Party which did not provide the Subcontract Works Information.

63.9 If a change to the Subcontract Works Information makes the description of the Condition for a Key Date incorrect, the *Contractor* corrects the description. This correction is taken into account in assessing the compensation event for the change to the Subcontract Works Information.

The *Contractor*'s **64**
assessments 64.1 The *Contractor* assesses a compensation event

- if the *Subcontractor* has not submitted a quotation and details of his assessment within the time allowed,
- if the *Contractor* decides that the *Subcontractor* has not assessed the compensation event correctly in a quotation and he does not instruct the *Subcontractor* to submit a revised quotation,
- if, when the *Subcontractor* submits quotations for a compensation event, he has not submitted a programme or alterations to a programme which this subcontract requires him to submit or
- if, when the *Subcontractor* submits quotations for a compensation event, the *Contractor* has not accepted the *Subcontractor*'s latest programme for one of the reasons stated in this subcontract.

64.2 The *Contractor* assesses a compensation event using his own assessment of the programme for the remaining work if

- there is no Accepted Programme or
- the *Subcontractor* has not submitted a programme or alterations to a programme for acceptance as required by this subcontract.

64.3 The *Contractor* notifies the *Subcontractor* of his assessment of a compensation event and gives him details of it within the period allowed for the *Subcontractor*'s submission of his quotation for the same event. This period starts when the need for the *Contractor*'s assessment becomes apparent.

64.4 If the *Contractor* does not assess a compensation event within the time allowed, the *Subcontractor* may notify the *Contractor* to this effect. If the *Subcontractor* submitted more than one quotation for the compensation event, he states in his notification which quotation he proposes is to be accepted. If the *Contractor* does not reply within three weeks of this notification the notification is treated as acceptance of the *Subcontractor*'s quotation by the *Contractor*.

Implementing **65**
compensation events 65.1 A compensation event is implemented when

- the *Contractor* notifies his acceptance of the *Subcontractor*'s quotation,
- the *Contractor* notifies the *Subcontractor* of his own assessment or
- a *Subcontractor*'s quotation is treated as having been accepted by the *Contractor*.

65.2 The assessment of a compensation event is not revised if a forecast upon which it is based is shown by later recorded information to have been wrong.

core
clauses

main
option clauses

secondary
option clauses

cost
components

subcontract
data

7 Title

The *Contractor*'s title to Plant and Materials **70**

70.1 Whatever title the *Subcontractor* has to Plant and Materials which is outsid the Working Areas passes to the *Contractor* if the *Contractor* has marked it a for this subcontract.

70.2 Whatever title the *Subcontractor* has to Plant and Materials passes to th *Contractor* if it has been brought within the Working Areas. The title to Plar and Materials passes back to the *Subcontractor* if it is removed from th Working Areas with the *Contractor*'s permission.

Marking Equipment, Plant and Materials outside the Working Areas **71**

71.1 The *Contractor* marks Equipment, Plant and Materials which are outside th Working Areas if

- this subcontract identifies them for payment and
- the *Subcontractor* has prepared them for marking as the Subcontra Works Information requires.

Removing Equipment **72**

72.1 The *Subcontractor* removes Equipment from the Site when it is no longe needed unless the *Contractor* allows it to be left in the *subcontract works*.

Objects and materials within the Site **73**

73.1 The *Subcontractor* has no title to an object of value or of historical or othe interest within the Site. The *Subcontractor* notifies the *Contractor* when suc an object is found and the *Contractor* instructs the *Subcontractor* how to dea with it. The *Subcontractor* does not move the object without instructions.

73.2 The *Subcontractor* has title to materials from excavation and demolition on as stated in the Subcontract Works Information.

core clauses

main option clauses

secondary option clauses

cost components

subcontract data

Risks and insurance

Employer's and *Contractor*'s risks	**80**	
	80.1	The following are *Employer*'s and *Contractor*'s risks.

- Claims, proceedings, compensation and costs payable which are due to

  - use or occupation of the Site by the *works* or for the purpose of the *works* which is the unavoidable result of the *works*,
  - negligence, breach of statutory duty or interference with any legal right by the *Employer* or the *Contractor* or by any person employed by or contracted to them except the *Subcontractor* or
  - a fault of the *Employer* or the *Contractor* or a fault in their designs.

- Loss of or damage to Plant and Materials supplied to the *Subcontractor* by the *Employer* or *Contractor*, or by Others on the *Employer*'s or *Contractor*'s behalf, until the *Subcontractor* has received and accepted them.
- Loss of or damage to the *works*, Plant and Materials due to

  - war, civil war, rebellion, revolution, insurrection, military or usurped power,
  - strikes, riots and civil commotion not confined to the *Subcontractor*'s employees or
  - radioactive contamination.

- Loss of or wear or damage to the parts of the *subcontract works* taken over by the *Contractor*, except loss, wear or damage occurring before the issue of the Defects Certificate which is due to

  - a Defect which existed at take over,
  - an event occurring before take over which was not itself an *Employer*'s or *Contractor*'s risk or
  - the activities of the *Subcontractor* on the Site after take over.

- Loss of or wear or damage to the *subcontract works* and any Equipment, Plant and Materials retained on the Site by the *Employer* or *Contractor* after a termination, except loss, wear or damage due to the activities of the *Subcontractor* on the Site after the termination.
- Additional *Employer*'s or *Contractor*'s risks stated in the Subcontract Data.

The *Subcontractor*'s risks	**81**	
	81.1	From the *subcontract starting date* until the Defects Certificate has been issued, the risks which are not carried by the *Employer* or the *Contractor* are carried by the *Subcontractor*.
Repairs	**82**	
	82.1	Until the Defects Certificate has been issued and unless otherwise instructed by the *Contractor*, the *Subcontractor* promptly replaces loss of and repairs damage to the *subcontract works*, Plant and Materials.
Indemnity	**83**	
	83.1	Each Party indemnifies the other against claims, proceedings, compensation and costs due to an event which is at his risk. The *Contractor* indemnifies the *Subcontractor* against all claims and liabilities against which the *Employer* indemnifies the *Contractor* under the main contract.
	83.2	The liability of the *Subcontractor* to indemnify the *Contractor* is reduced if events at the *Employer*'s or *Contractor*'s risk contributed to the claims, proceedings, compensation and costs. The reduction is in proportion to the extent that events which were at the *Employer*'s or *Contractor*'s risk contributed, taking into account each Party's responsibilities under this subcontract.

core clauses

main option clauses

secondary option clauses

cost components

subcontract data

83.3 The liability of the *Contractor* to indemnify the *Subcontractor* is reduced
events at the *Subcontractor*'s risk contributed to the claims, proceeding
compensation and costs. The reduction is in proportion to the extent th
events which were at the *Subcontractor*'s risk contributed, taking into accou
each Party's responsibilities under this subcontract.

Insurance cover **84**

84.1 The *Subcontractor* provides the insurances stated in the Insurance Tab
except any insurance which the *Employer* or the *Contractor* is to provide
stated in the Subcontract Data. The *Subcontractor* provides addition
insurances as stated in the Subcontract Data.s

84.2 The insurances are in the joint names of the Parties and provide cover f
events which are at the *Subcontractor*'s risk from the *subcontract starting da
until the Defects Certificate or a termination certificate has been issued.

INSURANCE TABLE

Insurance against	Minimum amount of cover or minimum limit of indemnity
Loss of or damage to the *subcontract works*, Plant and Materials	The replacement cost, including the amount stated in the Subcontract Data for the replacement of any Plant and Materials provided by the *Employer* or the *Contractor*
Loss of or damage to Equipment	The replacement cost
Liability for loss of or damage to property (except the *subcontract works*, Plant and Materials and Equipment) and liability for bodily injury to or death of a person (not an employee of the *Subcontractor*) caused by activity in connection with this subcontract	The amount stated in the Subcontract Data for any one event with cross liability so that the insurance applies to the Parties separately
Liability for death of or bodily injury to employees of the *Subcontractor* arising out of and in the course of their employment in connection with this subcontract	The greater of the amount required by the applicable law and the amount stated in the Subcontract Data for any one event

Insurance policies **85**

85.1 Before the *subcontract starting date* and on each renewal of the insuran
policy until the *defects date*, the *Subcontractor* submits to the *Contractor* f
acceptance certificates which state that the insurance required by th
subcontract is in force. The certificates are signed by the *Subcontracto
insurer or insurance broker. A reason for not accepting the certificates is th
they do not comply with this subcontract.

85.2 Insurance policies include a waiver by the insurers of their subrogation righ
against directors and other employees of every insured except where there
fraud.

85.3 The Parties comply with the terms and conditions of the insurance policies.

85.4 Any amount not recovered from an insurer is borne by the *Employer* or *Contra
tor* for events which are at their risk and by the *Subcontractor* for events whi
are at his risk.

f the *Subcontractor* does not insure **86**

86.1 The *Contractor* may insure a risk which this subcontract requires the *Subcontractor* to insure if the *Subcontractor* does not submit a required certificate. The cost of this insurance to the *Contractor* is paid by the *Subcontractor*.

surance by the *Employer* or the *Contractor* **87**

87.1 The *Contractor* submits policies and certificates for insurances provided by the *Employer* or the *Contractor* to the *Subcontractor* for acceptance before the *subcontract starting date* and afterwards as the *Subcontractor* instructs. The *Subcontractor* accepts the policies and certificates if they comply with this subcontract.

87.2 The *Subcontractor*'s acceptance of an insurance policy or certificate provided by the *Employer* or *Contractor* does not change the responsibility of the *Employer* or *Contractor* to provide the insurances stated in the Subcontract Data.

87.3 The *Subcontractor* may insure a risk which this subcontract requires the *Employer* or *Contractor* to insure if the *Contractor* does not submit a required policy or certificate. The cost of this insurance to the *Subcontractor* is paid by the *Contractor*.

9 Termination

Termination **90**

90.1 If either Party wishes to terminate the *Subcontractor*'s obligation to Provi◗ the Subcontract Works he notifies the other Party giving details of his reas◗ for terminating. The *Contractor* issues a termination certificate promptly if t◗ reason complies with this subcontract.

90.2 The *Subcontractor* may terminate only for a reason identified in the Termin◗ tion Table. The *Contractor* may terminate for any reason. The procedur◗ followed and the amounts due on termination are in accordance with t◗ Termination Table.

TERMINATION TABLE

Terminating Party	Reason	Procedure	Amount due
The *Contractor*	A reason other than R1–R21	P1 and P2	A1, A2 and A4
	R1–R15 or R18	P1, P2 and P3	A1 and A3
	R17 or R20	P1 and P3	A1 and A2
	R21	P1 and P4	A1 and A2
The *Subcontractor*	R1–R10, R16 or R19	P1 and P4	A1, A2 and A4
	R17 or R20	P1 and P4	A1 and A2

90.3 The procedures for termination are implemented immediately after t◗ *Contractor* has issued a termination certificate.

90.4 Within fourteen weeks of termination, the *Contractor* certifies a final payme◗ to or from the *Subcontractor* which is the *Contractor*'s assessment of t◗ amount due on termination less the total of previous payments. Payment ◗ made within four weeks of the *Contractor*'s certificate.

90.5 After a termination certificate has been issued, the *Subcontractor* does ◗ further work necessary to Provide the Subcontract Works.

Reasons for termination **91**

91.1 Either Party may terminate if the other Party has done one of the following ◗ its equivalent.

- If the other Party is an individual and has
  - presented his petition for bankruptcy (R1),
  - had a bankruptcy order made against him (R2),
  - had a receiver appointed over his assets (R3) or
  - made an arrangement with his creditors (R4).

- If the other Party is a company or partnership and has
  - had a winding-up order made against it (R5),
  - had a provisional liquidator appointed to it (R6),
  - passed a resolution for winding-up (other than in order to amalgama◗ or reconstruct) (R7),
  - had an administration order made against it (R8),
  - had a receiver, receiver and manager, or administrative receiv◗ appointed over the whole or a substantial part of its undertaking ◗ assets (R9) or
  - made an arrangement with its creditors (R10).

91.2 The *Contractor* may terminate if he has notified that the *Subcontractor* has defaulted in one of the following ways and not put the default right within three weeks of the notification.

- Substantially failed to comply with his obligations (R11).
- Not provided a bond or guarantee which this subcontract requires (R12).
- Appointed a Subsubcontractor for substantial work before the *Contractor* has accepted the Subsubcontractor (R13).

91.3 The *Contractor* may terminate if he has notified that the *Subcontractor* has defaulted in one of the following ways and not stopped defaulting within three weeks of the notification.

- Substantially hindered the *Employer,* the *Contractor* or Others (R14).
- Substantially broken a health or safety regulation (R15).

91.4 The *Subcontractor* may terminate if the *Contractor* has not paid an amount certified by him within thirteen weeks of the date of the certificate (R16).

91.5 Either Party may terminate if the Parties have been released under the law from further performance of the whole of this subcontract (R17).

91.6 If the *Contractor* has instructed the *Subcontractor* to stop or not to start any substantial work or all work and an instruction allowing the work to re-start or start has not been given within fourteen weeks,

- the *Contractor* may terminate if the instruction was due to a default by the *Subcontractor* (R18),
- the *Subcontractor* may terminate if the instruction was due to a default by the *Contractor* (R19) and
- either Party may terminate if the instruction was due to any other reason (R20).

91.7 The *Contractor* may terminate if an event occurs which

- stops the *Subcontractor* completing the *subcontract works* or
- stops the *Subcontractor* completing the *subcontract works* by the date shown on the Accepted Programme and is forecast to delay Completion by more than 13 weeks,

and which

- neither Party could prevent and
- an experienced subcontractor would have judged at the Subcontract Date to have such a small chance of occurring that it would have been unreasonable for him to have allowed for it (R21).

Procedures on termination 92

92.1 On termination, the *Contractor* may complete the *subcontract works* and may use any Plant and Materials to which he has title (P1).

92.2 The procedure on termination also includes one or more of the following as set out in the Termination Table.

P2 The *Contractor* may instruct the *Subcontractor* to leave the Site, remove any Equipment, Plant and Materials from the Site and assign the benefit of any subsubcontract or other contract related to performance of this subcontract to the *Contractor*.

P3 The *Contractor* may use any Equipment to which the *Subcontractor* has title to complete the *subcontract works*. The *Subcontractor* promptly removes the Equipment from Site when the *Contractor* notifies him that the *Contractor* no longer requires it to complete the *subcontract works*.

P4 The *Subcontractor* leaves the Working Areas and removes the Equipment.

Payment on termination **93**

93.1 The amount due on termination includes (A1)

- an amount due assessed as for normal payments,
- the Defined Cost for Plant and Materials

  - within the Working Areas or
  - to which the *Contractor* has title and of which the *Subcontractor* has accept delivery,

- other Defined Cost reasonably incurred in expectation of completing t whole of the *subcontract works*,
- any amounts retained by the *Contractor* and
- a deduction of any un-repaid balance of an advanced payment.

93.2 The amount due on termination also includes one or more of the following set out in the Termination Table.

A2 The forecast Defined Cost of removing the Equipment.

A3 A deduction of the forecast of the additional cost to the *Contractor* completing the whole of the *subcontract works*.

A4 The *direct fee percentage* applied to

- for Options A, B, C and D, any excess of the total of the Prices at the Su contract Date over the Price for Work Done to Date or
- for Option E any excess of the first forecast of the Defined Cost for t *subcontract works* over the Price for Work Done to Date less the Fee.

ption A: Priced subcontract with activity schedule

Identified and defined terms	**11** 11.2	(20) The Activity Schedule is the *activity schedule* unless later changed in accordance with this subcontract.

(22) Defined Cost is the cost of the components in the Shorter Schedule of Cost Components whether work is subsubcontracted or not excluding the cost of preparing quotations for compensation events.

(27) The Price for Work Done to Date is the total of the Prices for

- each group of completed activities and
- each completed activity which is not in a group.

A completed activity is one which is without Defects which would either delay or be covered by immediately following work.

(30) The Prices are the lump sum prices for each of the activities in the Activity Schedule unless later changed in accordance with this subcontract.

The programme **31**

31.4   The *Subcontractor* provides information which shows how each activity on the Activity Schedule relates to the operations on each programme which he submits for acceptance.

Acceleration **36**

36.3   When the *Contractor* accepts a quotation for an acceleration, he changes the Prices, the Subcontract Completion Date and the Key Dates accordingly and accepts the revised programme.

The Activity Schedule **54**

54.1   Information in the Activity Schedule is not Subcontract Works Information or Site Information.

54.2   If the *Subcontractor* changes a planned method of working at his discretion so that the activities on the Activity Schedule do not relate to the operations on the Accepted Programme, he submits a revision of the Activity Schedule to the *Contractor* for acceptance.

54.3   A reason for not accepting a revision of the Activity Schedule is that

- it does not comply with the Accepted Programme,
- any changed Prices are not reasonably distributed between the activities or
- the total of the Prices is changed.

Assessing compensation events **63**

63.10   If the effect of a compensation event is to reduce the total Defined Cost and the event is

- a change to the Subcontract Works Information or
- a correction of an assumption stated by the *Contractor* for assessing an earlier compensation event,

the Prices are reduced.

core clauses

main option clauses

secondary option clauses

cost components

subcontract data

63.12 Assessments for changed Prices for compensation events are in the form changes to the Activity Schedule.

63.14 If the *Contractor* and the *Subcontractor* agree, rates and lump sums may used to assess a compensation event instead of Defined Cost.

Implementing **65**
compensation events 65.4 The changes to the Prices, the Subcontract Completion Date and the Dates are included in the notification implementing a compensation event.

Payment on termination **93**
93.3 The amount due on termination is assessed without taking grouping activities into account.

ption B: Priced subcontract with bill of quantities

Identified and defined terms **11**

11.2 (21) The Bill of Quantities is the *bill of quantities* as changed in accordance with this subcontract to accommodate implemented compensation events and for accepted quotations for acceleration.

(22) Defined Cost is the cost of the components in the Shorter Schedule of Cost Components whether work is subsubcontracted or not excluding the cost of preparing quotations for compensation events.

(28) The Price for Work Done to Date is the total of

- the quantity of the work which the *Subcontractor* has completed for each item in the Bill of Quantities multiplied by the rate and
- a proportion of each lump sum which is the proportion of the work covered by the item which the *Subcontractor* has completed.

Completed work is work without Defects which would either delay or be covered by immediately following work.

(31) The Prices are the lump sums and the amounts obtained by multiplying the rates by the quantities for the items in the Bill of Quantities.

Acceleration **36**

36.3 When the *Contractor* accepts a quotation for an acceleration, he changes the Prices, the Subcontract Completion Date and the Key Dates accordingly and accepts the revised programme.

The Bill of Quantities **55**

55.1 Information in the Bill of Quantities is not Subcontract Works Information or Site Information.

Compensation events **60**

60.4 A difference between the final total quantity of work done and the quantity stated for an item in the Bill of Quantities is a compensation event if

- the difference does not result from a change to the Subcontract Works Information,
- the difference causes the Defined Cost per unit of quantity to change and
- the rate in the Bill of Quantities for the item multiplied by the final total quantity of work done is more than 0.5% of the total of the Prices at the Subcontract Date.

If the Defined Cost per unit of quantity is reduced, the affected rate is reduced.

60.5 A difference between the final total quantity of work done and the quantity for an item stated in the Bill of Quantities which delays Completion or the meeting of the Condition stated for a Key Date is a compensation event.

60.6 The *Contractor* corrects mistakes in the Bill of Quantities which are departures from the rules for item descriptions and for division of the work into items in the *method of measurement* or are due to ambiguities or inconsistencies. Each such correction is a compensation event which may lead to reduced Prices.

60.7 In assessing a compensation event which results from a correction of an inconsistency between the Bill of Quantities and another document, the *Subcontractor* is assumed to have taken the Bill of Quantities as correct.

core clauses

main option clauses

secondary option clauses

cost components

subcontract data

Assessing compensation **63**
events 63.10 If the effect of a compensation event is to reduce the total Defined Cost a the event is

- a change to the Subcontract Works Information or
- a correction of an assumption stated by the *Contractor* for assessing earlier compensation event,

the Prices are reduced.

63.13 Assessments for changed Prices for compensation events are in the form changes to the Bill of Quantities.

- For the whole or a part of a compensation event for work not yet dc and for which there is an item in the Bill of Quantities, the changes are

  - a changed rate,
  - a changed quantity or
  - a changed lump sum.

- For the whole or a part of a compensation event for work not yet done a for which there is no item in the Bill of Quantities, the change is a r priced item which, unless the *Contractor* and the *Subcontractor* ag otherwise, is compiled in accordance with the *method of measurement*.
- For the whole or a part of a compensation event for work already do the change is a new lump sum item.

If the *Contractor* and the *Subcontractor* agree, rates and lump sums may used to assess a compensation event instead of Defined Cost.

Implementing **65**
compensation events 65.4 The changes to the Prices, the Subcontract Completion Date and the k Dates are included in the notification implementing a compensation event.

ption C: Target subcontract with activity schedule

Identified and defined **11**
terms 11.2   (20) The Activity Schedule is the *activity schedule* unless later changed in accordance with this subcontract.

(23) Defined Cost is

- the amount of payments due to Subsubcontractors for work which is subsubcontracted without taking account of amounts deducted for

  - retention,
  - payment to the *Contractor* as a result of a Subsubcontractor failing to meet a Key Date,
  - correction of Defects after Completion,
  - payments to Others and
  - supply of equipment, supplies and services included in the charge for overhead cost within the Working Areas in this subcontract

and

- the cost of components in the Schedule of Cost Components for other work

less Disallowed Cost.

(25) Disallowed Cost is cost which the *Contractor* decides

- is not justified by the *Subcontractor*'s accounts and records,
- should not have been paid to a Subsubcontractor or supplier in accordance with his contract,
- was incurred only because the *Subcontractor* did not

  - follow an acceptance or procurement procedure stated in the Sub-contract Works Information or
  - give an early warning which this subcontract required him to give

and the cost of

- correcting Defects after Completion,
- correcting Defects caused by the *Subcontractor* not complying with a constraint on how he is to Provide the Subcontract Works stated in the Subcontract Works Information,
- Plant and Materials not used to Provide the Subcontract Works (after allowing for reasonable wastage) unless resulting from a change to the Subcontract Works Information,
- resources not used to Provide the Subcontract Works (after allowing for reasonable availability and utilisation) or not taken away from the Working Areas when the *Contractor* requested and
- preparation for and conduct of an adjudication or proceedings of the *tribunal*.

(29) The Price for Work Done to Date is the total Defined Cost which the *Contractor* forecasts will have been paid by the *Subcontractor* before the next assessment date plus the Fee.

(30) The Prices are the lump sum prices for each of the activities in the Activity Schedule unless later changed in accordance with this subcontract.

Providing the Subcontract **20**
Works 20.3   The *Subcontractor* advises the *Contractor* on the practical implications of the design of the *subcontract works* and on subsubcontracting arrangements.

core clauses

main option clauses

secondary option clauses

cost components

subcontract data

20.4   The *Subcontractor* prepares forecasts of the total Defined Cost for the wh of the *subcontract works* in consultation with the *Contractor* and submits th to the *Contractor*. Forecasts are prepared at the intervals stated in Subcontract Data from the *subcontract starting date* until Completion of whole of the *subcontract works*. An explanation of the changes made sir the previous forecast is submitted with each forecast.

Subsubcontracting 26

26.4   The *Subcontractor* submits the proposed contract data for each subsub tract for acceptance to the *Contractor* if

- an NEC contract is proposed and
- the *Contractor* instructs the *Subcontractor* to make the submission.

A reason for not accepting the proposed contract data is that its use will allow the *Subcontractor* to Provide the Subcontract Works.

The programme 31

31.4   The *Subcontractor* provides information which shows how each activity the Activity Schedule relates to the operations on each programme which submits for acceptance.

Acceleration 36

36.3   When the *Contractor* accepts a quotation for an acceleration, he changes Prices, the Subcontract Completion Date and the Key Dates accordingly a accepts the revised programme.

Tests and inspections 40

40.7   When the *Contractor* assesses the cost incurred by him in repeating a test inspection after a Defect is found, he does not include the *Subcontracto* cost of carrying out the repeat test or inspection.

Assessing the amount due 50

50.6   Payments of Defined Cost made by the *Subcontractor* in a currency other th the *currency of this subcontract* are included in the amount due as paymer to be made to him in the same currency. Such payments are converted to *currency of this subcontract* in order to calculate the Fee and any *Subc* tractor's share using the *exchange rates*.

Defined Cost 52

52.2   The *Subcontractor* keeps these records

- accounts of payments of Defined Cost,
- proof that the payments have been made,
- communications about and assessments of compensation events Subsubcontractors and
- other records as stated in the Subcontract Works Information.

52.3   The *Subcontractor* allows the *Contractor* to inspect at any time within worki hours the accounts and records which he is required to keep.

The *Subcontractor*'s share 53

53.1   The *Contractor* assesses the *Subcontractor*'s share of the difference betwe the total of the Prices and the Price for Work Done to Date. The difference divided into increments falling within each of the *share ranges*. The limits o *share range* are the Price for Work Done to Date divided by the total of Prices, expressed as a percentage. The *Subcontractor*'s share equals the s of the products of the increment within each *share range* and the correspor ing *Subcontractor's share percentage*.

53.2   If the Price for Work Done to Date is less than the total of the Prices, t *Subcontractor* is paid his share of the saving. If the Price for Work Done Date is greater than the total of the Prices, the *Subcontractor* pays his sha of the excess.

53.3 The *Contractor* makes a preliminary assessment of the *Subcontractor*'s share at Completion of the whole of the *subcontract works* using his forecasts of the final Price for Work Done to Date and the final total of the Prices. This share is included in the amount due following Completion of the whole of the *subcontract works*.

53.4 The *Contractor* makes a final assessment of the *Subcontractor*'s share using the final Price for Work Done to Date and the final total of the Prices. This share is included in the final amount due.

The Activity Schedule 54

54.1 Information in the Activity Schedule is not Subcontract Works Information or Site Information.

54.2 If the *Subcontractor* changes a planned method of working at his discretion so that the activities on the Activity Schedule do not relate to the operations on the Accepted Programme, he submits a revision of the Activity Schedule to the *Contractor* for acceptance.

54.3 A reason for not accepting a revision of the Activity Schedule is that

- it does not comply with the Accepted Programme,
- any changed Prices are not reasonably distributed between the activities or
- the total of the Prices is changed.

Assessing compensation 63
events

63.11 If the effect of a compensation event is to reduce the total Defined Cost and the event is

- a change to the Subcontract Works Information, other than a change to the Subcontract Works Information provided by the *Contractor* which the *Subcontractor* proposed and the *Contractor* has accepted or
- a correction of an assumption stated by the *Contractor* for assessing an earlier compensation event,

the Prices are reduced.

63.12 Assessments for changed Prices for compensation events are in the form of changes to the Activity Schedule.

63.15 If the *Contractor* and the *Subcontractor* agree, the *Subcontractor* assesses a compensation event using the Shorter Schedule of Cost Components. The *Contractor* may make his own assessments using the Shorter Schedule of Cost Components.

Implementing 65
compensation events

65.4 The changes to the Prices, the Subcontract Completion Date and the Key Dates are included in the notification implementing a compensation event.

Payment on termination 93

93.4 If there is a termination, the *Contractor* assesses the *Subcontractor*'s share after he has certified termination. His assessment uses, as the Price for Work Done to Date, the total of the Defined Cost which the *Subcontractor* has paid and which he is committed to pay for work done before termination. The assessment uses as the total of the Prices

- the lump sump price for each activity which has been completed and
- a proportion of the lump sum price for each incomplete activity which is the proportion of the work in the activity which has been completed.

93.6 The *Contractor*'s assessment of the *Subcontractor*'s share is added to the amount due to the *Subcontractor* on termination if there has been a saving or deducted if there has been an excess.

Option D: Target subcontract with bill of quantities

Identified and defined 11
terms 11.2

(21) The Bill of Quantities is the *bill of quantities* as changed in accordan with this subcontract to accommodate implemented compensation events a for accepted quotations for acceleration.

(23) Defined Cost is

- the amount of payments due to Subsubcontractors for work which subsubcontracted without taking account of amounts deducted for
  - retention,
  - payment to the *Contractor* as a result of a Subsubcontractor failing meet a Key Date,
  - the correction of Defects after Completion,
  - payments to Others and
  - the supply of equipment, supplies and services included in the char for overhead cost within the Working Areas in this subcontract

and

- the cost of components in the Schedule of Cost Components for oth work

less Disallowed Cost.

(25) Disallowed Cost is cost which the *Contractor* decides

- is not justified by the *Subcontractor*'s accounts and records,
- should not have been paid to a Subsubcontractor or supplier in accordan with his contract,
- was incurred only because the *Subcontractor* did not
  - follow an acceptance or procurement procedure stated in the Subcc tract Works Information or
  - give an early warning which this subcontract required him to give

and the cost of

- correcting Defects after Completion,
- correcting Defects caused by the *Subcontractor* not complying with constraint on how he is to Provide the Subcontract Works stated in t Subcontract Works Information,
- Plant and Materials not used to Provide the Subcontract Works (aft allowing for reasonable wastage) unless resulting from a change to t Subcontract Works Information,
- resources not used to Provide the Subcontract Works (after allowi for reasonable availability and utilisation) or not taken away from t Working Areas when the *Contractor* requested and
- preparation for and conduct of an adjudication or proceedings of t *tribunal*.

(29) The Price for Work Done to Date is the total Defined Cost which t *Contractor* forecasts will have been paid by the *Subcontractor* before the ne assessment date plus the Fee.

(31) The Prices are the lump sums and the amounts obtained by multiplyi the rates by the quantities for the items in the Bill of Quantities.

(33) The Total of the Prices is the total of

- the quantity of the work which the *Subcontractor* has completed for each item in the Bill of Quantities multiplied by the rate and
- a proportion of each lump sum which is the proportion of the work covered by the item which the *Subcontractor* has completed.

Completed work is work without Defects which would either delay or be covered by immediately following work.

Providing the Subcontract Works **20**

20.3   The *Subcontractor* advises the *Contractor* on the practical implications of the design of the *subcontract works* and on subsubcontracting arrangements.

20.4   The *Subcontractor* prepares forecasts of the total Defined Cost for the whole of the *subcontract works* in consultation with the *Contractor* and submits them to the *Contractor*. Forecasts are prepared at the intervals stated in the Subcontract Data from the *subcontract starting date* until Completion of the whole of the *subcontract works*. An explanation of the changes made since the previous forecast is submitted with each forecast.

Subsubcontracting **26**

26.4   The *Subcontractor* submits the proposed contract data for each subsubcontract for acceptance to the *Contractor* if

- an NEC contract is proposed and
- the *Contractor* instructs the *Subcontractor* to make the submission.

A reason for not accepting the proposed contract data is that its use will not allow the *Subcontractor* to Provide the Subcontract Works.

Acceleration **36**

36.3   When the *Contractor* accepts a quotation for an acceleration, he changes the Prices, the Subcontract Completion Date and the Key Dates accordingly and accepts the revised programme.

Tests and inspections **40**

40.7   When the *Contractor* assesses the cost incurred by him in repeating a test or inspection after a Defect is found, he does not include the *Subcontractor*'s cost of carrying out the repeat test or inspection.

Assessing the amount due **50**

50.6   Payments of Defined Cost made by the *Subcontractor* in a currency other than the *currency of this subcontract* are included in the amount due as payments to be made to him in the same currency. Such payments are converted to the *currency of this subcontract* in order to calculate the Fee and any *Subcontractor*'s share using the *exchange rates.*

Defined Cost **52**

52.2   The *Subcontractor* keeps these records

- accounts of payments of Defined Cost,
- proof that the payments have been made,
- communications about and assessments of compensation events for Subsubcontractors and
- other records as stated in the Subcontract Works Information.

52.3   The *Subcontractor* allows the *Contractor* to inspect at any time within working hours the accounts and records which he is required to keep.

core clauses

main option clauses

secondary option clauses

cost components

subcontract data

The *Subcontractor*'s share **53**

53.5 The *Contractor* assesses the *Subcontractor*'s share of the difference betwe the Total of the Prices and the Price for Work Done to Date. The difference divided into increments falling within each of the *share ranges*. The limits o *share range* are the Price for Work Done to Date divided by the Total of 1 Prices, expressed as a percentage. The *Subcontractor*'s share equals the s of the products of the increment within each *share range* and the correspor ing *Subcontractor's share percentage*.

53.6 If the Price for Work Done to Date is less than the Total of the Prices, t *Subcontractor* is paid his share of the saving. If the Price for Work Done Date is greater than the Total of the Prices, the *Subcontractor* pays his sh of the excess.

53.7 The *Contractor* makes a preliminary assessment of the *Subcontractor*'s sh at Completion of the whole of the *subcontract works* using his forecasts of 1 final Price for Work Done to Date and the final Total of the Prices. This sh is included in the amount due following Completion of the whole of 1 *subcontract works*.

53.8 The *Contractor* makes a final assessment of the *Subcontractor*'s share usi the final Price for Work Done to Date and the final Total of the Prices. T share is included in the final amount due.

The Bill of Quantities **55**

55.1 Information in the Bill of Quantities is not Subcontract Works Information Site Information.

Compensation events **60**

60.4 A difference between the final total quantity of work done and the quant stated for an item in the Bill of Quantities is a compensation event if

- the difference does not result from a change to the Subcontract Wor Information,
- the difference causes the Defined Cost per unit of quantity to chan and
- the rate in the Bill of Quantities for the item multiplied by the final to quantity of work done is more than 0.5% of the total of the Prices at t Subcontract Date.

If the Defined Cost per unit of quantity is reduced, the affected rate reduced.

60.5 A difference between the final total quantity of work done and the quantity an item stated in the Bill of Quantities which delays Completion or the me ing of the Condition stated for a Key Date is a compensation event.

60.6 The *Contractor* corrects mistakes in the Bill of Quantities which are departur from the rules for item descriptions and for division of the work into items the *method of measurement* or are due to ambiguities or inconsistenci Each such correction is a compensation event which may lead to reduc Prices.

60.7 In assessing a compensation event which results from a correction of inconsistency between the Bill of Quantities and another document, t *Subcontractor* is assumed to have taken the Bill of Quantities as correct.

Assessing compensation events **63**

63.11 If the effect of a compensation event is to reduce the total Defined Cost and the event is

- a change to the Subcontract Works Information, other than a change to the Subcontract Works Information provided by the *Contractor* which the *Subcontractor* proposed and the *Contractor* has accepted or
- a correction of an assumption stated by the *Contractor* for assessing an earlier compensation event,

the Prices are reduced.

63.13 Assessments for changed Prices for compensation events are in the form of changes to the Bill of Quantities.

- For the whole or a part of a compensation event for work not yet done and for which there is an item in the Bill of Quantities, the changes are

  - a changed rate,
  - a changed quantity or
  - a changed lump sum.

- For the whole or a part of a compensation event for work not yet done and for which there is no item in the Bill of Quantities, the change is a new priced item which, unless the *Contractor* and the *Subcontractor* agree otherwise, is compiled in accordance with the *method of measurement*.
- For the whole or a part of a compensation event for work already done, the change is a new lump sum item.

If the *Contractor* and the *Subcontractor* agree, rates and lump sums may be used to assess a compensation event instead of Defined Cost.

63.15 If the *Contractor* and the *Subcontractor* agree, the *Subcontractor* assesses a compensation event using the Shorter Schedule of Cost Components. The *Contractor* may make his own assessments using the Shorter Schedule of Cost Components.

Implementing compensation events **65**

65.4 The changes to the Prices, the Subcontract Completion Date and the Key Dates are included in the notification implementing a compensation event.

Payment on termination **93**

93.5 If there is a termination, the *Contractor* assesses the *Subcontractor*'s share after he has certified termination. His assessment uses, as the Price for Work Done to Date, the total of the Defined Cost which the *Subcontractor* has paid and which he is committed to pay for work done before termination.

93.6 The *Contractor*'s assessment of the *Subcontractor*'s share is added to the amount due to the *Subcontractor* on termination if there has been a saving or deducted if there has been an excess.

core clauses

main option clauses

secondary option clauses

cost components

subcontract data

Option E: Cost reimbursable subcontract

Identified and defined **11**
terms 11.2   (23) Defined Cost is

- the amount of payments due to Subsubcontractors for work which
  subsubcontracted without taking account of amounts deducted for

  - retention,
  - payment to the *Contractor* as a result of a Subsubcontractor failing
    meet a Key Date,
  - the correction of Defects after Completion,
  - payments to Others and
  - the supply of equipment, supplies and services included in the charg
    for overhead cost within the Working Areas in this subcontract

and

- the cost of components in the Schedule of Cost Components for othe
  work

less Disallowed Cost.

(25) Disallowed Cost is cost which the *Contractor* decides

- is not justified by the *Subcontractor*'s accounts and records,
- should not have been paid to a Subsubcontractor or supplier in accordanc
  with his contract,
- was incurred only because the *Subcontractor* did not

  - follow an acceptance or procurement procedure stated in the Sub
    contract Works Information or
  - give an early warning which this subcontract required him to give

and the cost of

- correcting Defects after Completion,
- correcting Defects caused by the *Subcontractor* not complying with
  constraint on how he is to Provide the Subcontract Works stated in th
  Subcontract Works Information,
- Plant and Materials not used to Provide the Subcontract Works (afte
  allowing for reasonable wastage) unless resulting from a change to th
  Subcontract Works Information,
- resources not used to Provide the Subcontract Works (after allowing fc
  reasonable availability and utilisation) or not taken away from th
  Working Areas when the *Contractor* requested and
- preparation for and conduct of an adjudication or proceedings of th
  tribunal.

(29) The Price for Work Done to Date is the total Defined Cost which th
Contractor forecasts will have been paid by the *Subcontractor* before the nex
assessment date plus the Fee.

(32) The Prices are the Defined Cost plus the Fee.

Providing the Subcontract **20**
Works
20.3   The *Subcontractor* advises the *Contractor* on the practical implications of th
design of the *subcontract works* and on subsubcontracting arrangements.

20.4   The *Subcontractor* prepares forecasts of the total Defined Cost for the whol
of the *subcontract works* in consultation with the *Contractor* and submit
them to the *Contractor*. Forecasts are prepared at the intervals stated in th
Subcontract Data from the *subcontract starting date* until Completion of th
whole of the *subcontract works*. An explanation of the changes made sinc

core
clauses

main
option clauses

secondary
option clauses

cost
components

subcontract
data

the previous forecast is submitted with each forecast.

Subsubcontracting **26**

26.4 The *Subcontractor* submits the proposed contract data for each subsubcontract for acceptance to the *Contractor* if

- an NEC contract is proposed and
- the *Contractor* instructs the *Subcontractor* to make the submission.

A reason for not accepting the proposed contract data is that its use will not allow the *Subcontractor* to Provide the Subcontract Works.

Acceleration **36**

36.4 When the *Contractor* accepts a quotation for an acceleration, he changes the Subcontract Completion Date, the Key Dates and the forecast of the total Defined Cost of the whole of the *subcontract works* accordingly and accepts the revised programme.

Tests and inspections **40**

40.7 When the *Contractor* assesses the cost incurred by him in repeating a test or inspection after a Defect is found, he does not include the *Subcontractor*'s cost of carrying out the repeat test or inspection.

Assessing the amount due **50**

50.7 Payments of Defined Cost made by the *Subcontractor* in a currency other than the *currency of this subcontract* are included in the amount due as payments to be made to him in the same currency. Such payments are converted to the *currency of this subcontract* in order to calculate the Fee using the *exchange rates.*

Defined Cost **52**

52.2 The *Subcontractor* keeps these records

- accounts of payments of Defined Cost,
- proof that the payments have been made,
- communications about and assessments of compensation events for Subsubcontractors and
- other records as stated in the Subcontract Works Information.

52.3 The *Subcontractor* allows the *Contractor* to inspect at any time within working hours the accounts and records which he is required to keep.

Assessing compensation events **63**

63.15 If the *Contractor* and the *Subcontractor* agree, the *Subcontractor* assesses a compensation event using the Shorter Schedule of Cost Components. The *Contractor* may make his own assessments using the Shorter Schedule of Cost Components.

Implementing compensation events **65**

65.3 The changes to the forecast amount of the Prices, the Subcontract Completion Date and the Key Dates are included in the notification implementing a compensation event.

DISPUTE RESOLUTION

Option W1

Dispute resolution procedure (used unless the United Kingdom Housing Grants, Construction and Regeneration A 1996 applies).

core clauses	
main option clauses	
secondary option clauses	
cost components	
subcontract data	

Dispute resolution **W1**

W1.1   A dispute arising under or in connection with this subcontract is referred and decided by the *Adjudicator*.

The *Adjudicator*   W1.2   (1) The Parties appoint the *Adjudicator* under the NEC Adjudicator's Contra current at the *subcontract starting date*.

(2) The *Adjudicator* acts impartially and decides the dispute as an indepe dent adjudicator and not as an arbitrator.

(3) If the *Adjudicator* is not identified in the Subcontract Data or if the *Adjudic tor* resigns or is unable to act, the Parties choose a new adjudicator jointly. If t Parties have not chosen an adjudicator, either Party may ask the *Adjudicat nominating body* to choose one. The *Adjudicator nominating body* chooses adjudicator within four days of the request. The chosen adjudicator becomes t *Adjudicator*.

(4) A replacement *Adjudicator* has the power to decide a dispute referred his predecessor but not decided at the time when the predecessor resigned became unable to act. He deals with an undecided dispute as if it had bee referred to him on the date he was appointed.

(5) The *Adjudicator*, his employees and agents are not liable to the Parties f any action or failure to take action in an adjudication unless the action or fa ure to take action was in bad faith.

The adjudication   W1.3   (1) Disputes are notified and referred to the *Adjudicator* in accordance wi the Adjudication Table.

ADJUDICATION TABLE

Dispute about	Which Party may refer it to the *Adjudicator*?	When may it be referred to the *Adjudicator*?
An action of the *Contractor*	The *Subcontractor*	Between two and four weeks after the *Subcontractor*'s notification of the dispute to the *Contractor*, the notification itself being made not more than four weeks after the *Subcontractor* becomes aware of the action
The *Contractor* not having taken an action	The *Subcontractor*	Between two and four weeks after the *Subcontractor*'s notification of the dispute to the *Contractor*, the notification itself being made not more than four weeks after the *Subcontractor* becomes aware that the action was not taken
A quotation for a compensation event which is treated as having been accepted	The *Contractor*	Between two and four weeks after the *Contractor*'s notification of the dispute to the *Subcontractor*, the notification itself being made not more than four weeks after the quotation was treated as accepted
Any other matter	Either Party	Between two and four weeks after notification of the dispute to the other Party

(2) The times for notifying and referring a dispute may be extended by the *Contractor* if the *Subcontractor* and the *Contractor* agree to the extension before the notice or referral is due. The *Contractor* notifies the extension that has been agreed to the *Subcontractor*. If a disputed matter is not notified and referred within the times set out in this subcontract, neither Party may subsequently refer it to the *Adjudicator* or the *tribunal*.

(3) The Party referring the dispute to the *Adjudicator* includes with his referral information to be considered by the *Adjudicator*. Any more information from a Party to be considered by the *Adjudicator* is provided within four weeks of the referral. This period may be extended if the *Adjudicator* and the Parties agree.

(4a) If a matter disputed by the *Subcontractor* under or in connection with a subsubcontract is also a matter disputed under or in connection with this subcontract and if the subsubcontract allows, the *Subcontractor* may refer the subsubcontract dispute to the *Adjudicator* at the same time as the subcontract referral. The *Adjudicator* then decides the disputes together and references to the Parties for the purposes of the dispute are interpreted as including the Subsubcontractor.

(4b) Within two weeks of the notification of the dispute by the *Subcontractor* to the *Contractor*, the *Contractor* notifies the *Subcontractor* if the matter disputed is a matter disputed under or in connection with the main contract.

The *Contractor* may then

- submit the subcontract dispute to the *main contract Adjudicator* at the same time as the main contract submission and
- instruct the *Subcontractor* to provide any information which the *Contractor* may require.

The *main contract Adjudicator* then decides the disputes together.

(5) The *Adjudicator* may

- review and revise any action or inaction of the *Contractor* related to dispute and alter a quotation which has been treated as having be accepted,
- take the initiative in ascertaining the facts and the law related to dispute,
- instruct a Party to provide further information related to the disp within a stated time and
- instruct a Party to take any other action which he considers necessary reach his decision and to do so within a stated time.

(6) A communication between a Party and the *Adjudicator* is communicated the other Party at the same time.

(7) If the *Adjudicator*'s decision includes assessment of additional cost delay caused to the *Subcontractor*, he makes his assessment in the sa way as a compensation event is assessed.

(8) The *Adjudicator* decides the dispute and notifies the Parties of his decis and his reasons within four weeks of the end of the period for receiv information. This four week period may be extended if the Parties agree.

(9) Unless and until the *Adjudicator* has notified the Parties of his decisi the Parties, the *Contractor* and the *Subcontractor* proceed as if the mat disputed was not disputed.

(10) The *Adjudicator*'s decision is binding on the Parties unless and u revised by the *tribunal* and is enforceable as a matter of contractual obligat between the Parties and not as an arbitral award. The *Adjudicator*'s decis is final and binding if neither Party has notified the other within the tin required by this subcontract that he is dissatisfied with a decision of *Adjudicator* and intends to refer the matter to the *tribunal*.

(11) The *Adjudicator* may, within two weeks of giving his decision to Parties, correct any clerical mistake or ambiguity.

Review by the *tribunal* W1.4

(1) A Party does not refer any dispute under or in connection with this s contract to the *tribunal* unless it has first been referred to the *Adjudicator* accordance with this subcontract.

(2) If, after the *Adjudicator* notifies his decision a Party is dissatisfied, he m notify the other Party that he intends to refer it to the *tribunal*. A Party may refer a dispute to the *tribunal* unless this notification is given within f weeks of notification of the *Adjudicator*'s decision.

(3) If the *Adjudicator* does not notify his decision within the time provided this subcontract, a Party may notify the other Party that he intends to re the dispute to the *tribunal*. A Party may not refer a dispute to the *tribu* unless this notification is given within four weeks of the date by which t *Adjudicator* should have notified his decision.

(4) The *tribunal* settles the dispute referred to it. The *tribunal* has the pow to reconsider any decision of the *Adjudicator* and review and revise any acti or inaction of the *Contractor* related to the dispute. A Party is not limited the *tribunal* proceedings to the information, evidence or arguments put to t *Adjudicator*.

(5) If the *tribunal* is arbitration, the *arbitration procedure*, the place where t arbitration is to be held and the method of choosing the arbitrator are tho stated in the Subcontract Data.

(6) A Party does not call the *Adjudicator* as a witness in *tribunal* proceeding

ption W2

spute resolution procedure (used in the United Kingdom when the Housing Grants, Construction and Regeneration
t 1996 applies).

Dispute resolution	**W2**	
	W2.1	(1) Any dispute arising under or in connection with this subcontract is referred to and decided by the *Adjudicator*. A Party may refer a dispute to the *Adjudicator* at any time.

(2) In this Option, time periods stated in days exclude Christmas Day, Good Friday and bank holidays.

The *Adjudicator* W2.2 (1) The Parties appoint the *Adjudicator* under the NEC Adjudicator's Contract current at the *subcontract starting date*.

(2) The *Adjudicator* acts impartially and decides the dispute as an independent adjudicator and not as an arbitrator.

(3) If the *Adjudicator* is not identified in the Subcontract Data or if the *Adjudicator* resigns or becomes unable to act

- the Parties may choose an adjudicator jointly or
- a Party may ask the *Adjudicator nominating body* to choose an adjudicator.

The *Adjudicator nominating body* chooses an adjudicator within four days of the request. The chosen adjudicator becomes the *Adjudicator*.

(4) A replacement *Adjudicator* has the power to decide a dispute referred to his predecessor but not decided at the time when his predecessor resigned or became unable to act. He deals with an undecided dispute as if it had been referred to him on the date he was appointed.

(5) The *Adjudicator,* his employees and agents are not liable to the Parties for any action or failure to take action in an adjudication unless the action or failure to take action was in bad faith.

The adjudication W2.3 (1) Before a Party refers a dispute to the *Adjudicator*, he gives a notice of adjudication to the other Party with a brief description of the dispute and the decision which he wishes the *Adjudicator* to make. If the *Adjudicator* is named in the Subcontract Data, the Party sends a copy of the notice of adjudication to the *Adjudicator* when it is issued. Within three days of the receipt of the notice of adjudication, the *Adjudicator* notifies the Parties

- that he is able to decide the dispute in accordance with the subcontract or
- that he is unable to decide the dispute and has resigned.

If the *Adjudicator* does not so notify within three days of the issue of the notice of adjudication, either Party may act as if he has resigned.

(2) Within seven days of a Party giving a notice of adjudication he

- refers the dispute to the *Adjudicator*,
- provides the *Adjudicator* with the information on which he relies, including any supporting documents and
- provides a copy of the information and supporting documents he has provided to the *Adjudicator* to the other Party.

Any further information from a Party to be considered by the *Adjudicator* is provided within fourteen days of the referral. This period may be extended if the *Adjudicator* and the Parties agree.

core clauses

main option clauses

secondary option clauses

cost components

subcontract data

(3a) If a matter disputed by the *Subcontractor* under or in connection with subsubcontract is also a matter disputed under or in connection with this su contract, the *Subcontractor* may, with the consent of the Subsubcontract refer the subsubcontract dispute to the *Adjudicator* at the same time as t subcontract referral. The *Adjudicator* then decides the disputes together a references to the Parties for the purposes of the dispute are interpreted including the Subsubcontractor.

(3b) Within two weeks of the notification of the dispute by the *Subcontrac* to the *Contractor*, the *Contractor* notifies the *Subcontractor* if the mat disputed is a matter disputed under or in connection with the main contract

The *Contractor* may, with the consent of the *Subcontractor*, then

- submit the subcontract dispute to the *main contract Adjudicator* at t same time as the main contract submission and
- instruct the *Subcontractor* to provide any information which the *Contrac* may require.

The *main contract Adjudicator* then settles the two disputes together.

(4) The *Adjudicator* may

- review and revise any action or inaction of the *Contractor* related to t dispute and alter a quotation which has been treated as having be accepted,
- take the initiative in ascertaining the facts and the law related to t dispute,
- instruct a Party to provide further information related to the dispu within a stated time and
- instruct a Party to take any other action which he considers necessary reach his decision and to do so within a stated time.

(5) If a Party does not comply with any instruction within the time stated the *Adjudicator,* the *Adjudicator* may continue the adjudication and make I decision based upon the information and evidence he has received.

(6) A communication between a Party and the *Adjudicator* is communicated the other Party at the same time.

(7) If the *Adjudicator*'s decision includes assessment of additional cost delay caused to the *Subcontractor,* he makes his assessment in the sar way as a compensation event is assessed.

(8) The *Adjudicator* decides the dispute and notifies the Parties of his decisi and his reasons within twenty-eight days of the dispute being referred to hi This period may be extended by up to fourteen days with the consent of t referring Party or by any other period agreed by the Parties.

(9) Unless and until the *Adjudicator* has notified the Parties of his decisic the Parties proceed as if the matter disputed was not disputed.

(10) If the *Adjudicator* does not make his decision and notify it to the Parti within the time provided by this subcontract, the Parties and the *Adjudica* may agree to extend the period for making his decision. If they do not agr to an extension, either Party may act as if the *Adjudicator* has resigned.

(11) The *Adjudicator*'s decision is binding on the Parties unless and ur revised by the *tribunal* and is enforceable as a matter of contractual obligati between the Parties and not as an arbitral award. The *Adjudicator*'s decisi is final and binding if neither Party has notified the other within the tim required by this subcontract that he is dissatisfied with a matter decided the *Adjudicator* and intends to refer the matter to the *tribunal*.

(12) The *Adjudicator* may, within fourteen days of giving his decision to t Parties, correct a clerical mistake or ambiguity.

Review by the *tribunal* W2.4

(1) A Party does not refer any dispute under or in connection with this sub-contract to the *tribunal* unless it has first been decided by the *Adjudicator* in accordance with this subcontract.

(2) If, after the *Adjudicator* notifies his decision a Party is dissatisfied, that Party may notify the other Party of the matter which he disputes and state that he intends to refer it to the *tribunal*. The dispute may not be referred to the *tribunal* unless this notification is given within four weeks of the notification of the *Adjudicator's* decision.

(3) The *tribunal* settles the dispute referred to it. The *tribunal* has the powers to reconsider any decision of the *Adjudicator* and to review and revise any action or inaction of the *Contractor* related to the dispute. A Party is not limited in *tribunal* proceedings to the information or evidence put to the *Adjudicator*.

(4) If the *tribunal* is arbitration, the *arbitration procedure,* the place where the arbitration is to be held and the method of choosing the arbitrator are those stated in the Subcontract Data.

(5) A Party does not call the *Adjudicator* as a witness in *tribunal* proceedings.

core clauses

main option clauses

secondary option clauses

cost components

subcontract data

SECONDARY OPTION CLAUSES

Option X1: Price adjustment for inflation (used only with Options A, B, C and D)

core
clauses

main
option clauses

secondary
option clauses

cost
components

subcontract
data

Defined terms **X1**

X1.1   (a) The Base Date Index (B) is the latest available index before the *base date*

(b) The Latest Index (L) is the latest available index before the date of assessment of an amount due.

(c) The Price Adjustment Factor is the total of the products of each of the proportions stated in the Subcontract Data multiplied by $(L - B)/B$ for the index linked to it.

Price Adjustment Factor X1.2   If an index is changed after it has been used in calculating a Price Adjustment Factor, the calculation is repeated and a correction included in the next assessment of the amount due.

The Price Adjustment Factor calculated at the Subcontract Completion Date for the whole of the *subcontract works* is used for calculating price adjustment after this date.

Compensation events X1.3   The Defined Cost for compensation events is assessed using the

- Defined Cost current at the time of assessing the compensation event adjusted to *base date* by dividing by one plus the Price Adjustment Factor for the last assessment of the amount due and
- Defined Cost at *base date* levels for amounts calculated from rates stated in the Subcontract Data for employees and Equipment.

Price adjustment Options A and B X1.4   Each amount due includes an amount for price adjustment which is the sum of

- the change in the Price for Work Done to Date since the last assessment of the amount due multiplied by the Price Adjustment Factor for the date of the current assessment,
- the amount for price adjustment included in the previous amount due and
- correcting amounts, not included elsewhere, which arise from changes to indices used for assessing previous amounts for price adjustment.

Price adjustment Options C and D X1.5   Each time the amount due is assessed, an amount for price adjustment is added to the total of the Prices which is the sum of

- the change in the Price for Work Done to Date since the last assessment of the amount due multiplied by $(PAF/(1 + PAF))$ where PAF is the Price Adjustment Factor for the date of the current assessment and
- correcting amounts, not included elsewhere, which arise from changes to indices used for assessing previous amounts for price adjustment.

Option X2: Changes in the law

Changes in the law X2

X2.1   A change in the law of the country in which the Site is located is a compensation event if it occurs after the Subcontract Date. The *Contractor* may notify the *Subcontractor* of a compensation event for a change in the law and instruct him to submit quotations. If the effect of a compensation event which is a change in the law is to reduce the total Defined Cost, the Prices are reduced.

Option X3: Multiple currencies (used only with Options A and B)

Multiple currencies X3

X3.1   The *Subcontractor* is paid in currencies other than the *currency of this subcontract* for the items or activities listed in the Subcontract Data. The *exchange rates* are used to convert from the *currency of this subcontract* to other currencies.

X3.2   Payments to the *Subcontractor* in currencies other than the *currency of this subcontract* do not exceed the maximum amounts stated in the Subcontract Data. Any excess is paid in the *currency of this subcontract.*

Option X4: Parent company guarantee

**Parent company X4
guarantee** X4.1   If a parent company owns the *Subcontractor*, the *Subcontractor* gives to the *Contractor* a guarantee by the parent company of the *Subcontractor*'s performance in the form set out in the Subcontract Works Information. If the guarantee was not given by the Subcontract Date, it is given to the *Contractor* within four weeks of the Subcontract Date.

Option X5: Sectional Completion

Sectional Completion X5

X5.1   In these *conditions of subcontract*, unless stated as the whole of the *subcontract works*, each reference and clause relevant to

- the *subcontract works*,
- Completion and
- Subcontract Completion Date

applies, as the case may be, to either the whole of the *subcontract works* or any *section* of the *subcontract works*.

core
clauses

main
option clauses

secondary
option clauses

cost
components

subcontract
data

nec 3 Engineering and Construction Subcontract

Option X6: Bonus for early Completion

Bonus for early Completion **X6**

X6.1 The *Subcontractor* is paid a bonus calculated at the rate stated in t Subcontract Data for each day from the earlier of

- Completion and
- the date on which the *Contractor* takes over the *subcontract works*

until the Subcontract Completion Date.

Option X7: Delay damages

Delay damages **X7**

X7.1 The *Subcontractor* pays delay damages at the rate stated in the Subcontra Data from the Subcontract Completion Date for each day until the earlier of

- Completion and
- the date on which the *Contractor* takes over the *subcontract works*.

X7.2 If the Subcontract Completion Date is changed to a later date after del damages have been paid, the *Contractor* repays the overpayment of damag with interest. Interest is assessed from the date of payment to the date repayment and the date of repayment is an assessment date.

X7.3 If the *Contractor* takes over a part of the *subcontract works* before Completio the delay damages are reduced from the date on which the part is taken ov The *Contractor* assesses the benefit of taking over the part of the *subcontra works* as a proportion of the benefit of taking over the whole of t *subcontract works* not previously taken over. The delay damages are reduc in this proportion.

Option X12: Partnering

Identified and defined **X12**
terms X12.1 (1) The Partners are those named in the Schedule of Partners. The *Client* is Partner.

(2) An Own Contract is a contract between two Partners which includes th Option.

(3) The Core Group comprises the Partners listed in the Schedule of Co Group Members.

(4) Partnering Information is information which specifies how the Partne work together and is either in the documents which the Subcontract Da states it is in or in an instruction given in accordance with this subcontract.

(5) A Key Performance Indicator is an aspect of performance for which target is stated in the Schedule of Partners.

Left margin tabs: core clauses / main option clauses / secondary option clauses / cost components / subcontract data

Actions X12.2 (1) Each Partner works with the other Partners to achieve the *Client*'s *objective* stated in the Subcontract Data and the objectives of every other Partner stated in the Schedule of Partners.

(2) Each Partner nominates a representative to act for it in dealings with other Partners.

(3) The Core Group acts and takes decisions on behalf of the Partners on those matters stated in the Partnering Information.

(4) The Partners select the members of the Core Group. The Core Group decides how they will work and decides the dates when each member joins and leaves the Core Group. The *Client*'s representative leads the Core Group unless stated otherwise in the Partnering Information.

(5) The Core Group keeps the Schedule of Core Group Members and the Schedule of Partners up to date and issues copies of them to the Partners each time either is revised.

(6) This Option does not create a legal partnership between Partners who are not one of the Parties in this subcontract.

Working together X12.3 (1) The Partners work together as stated in the Partnering Information and in a spirit of mutual trust and co-operation.

(2) A Partner may ask another Partner to provide information which he needs to carry out the work in his Own Contract and the other Partner provides it.

(3) Each Partner gives an early warning to the other Partners when he becomes aware of any matter that could affect the achievement of another Partner's objectives stated in the Schedule of Partners.

(4) The Partners use common information systems as set out in the Partnering Information.

(5) A Partner implements a decision of the Core Group by issuing instructions in accordance with its Own Contracts.

(6) The Core Group may give an instruction to the Partners to change the Partnering Information. Each such change to the Partnering Information is a compensation event which may lead to reduced Prices.

(7) The Core Group prepares and maintains a timetable showing the proposed timing of the contributions of the Partners. The Core Group issues a copy of the timetable to the Partners each time it is revised. The *Subcontractor* changes his programme if it is necessary to do so in order to comply with the revised timetable. Each such change is a compensation event which may lead to reduced Prices.

(8) A Partner gives advice, information and opinion to the Core Group and to other Partners when asked to do so by the Core Group. This advice, information and opinion relates to work that another Partner is to carry out under its Own Contract and is given fully, openly and objectively. The Partners show contingency and risk allowances in information about costs, prices and timing for future work.

(9) A Partner notifies the Core Group before subsubcontracting any work.

Incentives X12.4 (1) A Partner is paid the amount stated in the Schedule of Partners if the target stated for a Key Performance Indicator is improved upon or achieved. Payment of the amount is due when the target has been improved upon or achieved and is made as part of the amount due in the Partner's Own Contract.

(2) The *Client* may add a Key Performance Indicator and associated payment to the Schedule of Partners but may not delete or reduce a payment stated in the Schedule of Partners.

core clauses

main option clauses

secondary option clauses

cost components

subcontract data

Option X13: Performance bond

Performance bond **X13**

X13.1 The *Subcontractor* gives the *Contractor* a performance bond, provided by
bank or insurer which the *Contractor* has accepted, for the amount stated
the Subcontract Data and in the form set out in the Subcontract Works Inf
mation. A reason for not accepting the bank or insurer is that its commerc
position is not strong enough to carry the bond. If the bond was not given
the Subcontract Date, it is given to the *Contractor* within four weeks of t
Subcontract Date.

Option X14: Advanced payment to the *Subcontractor*

Advanced payment **X14**

X14.1 The *Contractor* makes an advanced payment to the *Subcontractor* of t
amount stated in the Subcontract Data.

X14.2 The advanced payment is made either within five weeks of the Subcontra
Date or, if an advanced payment bond is required, within five weeks of t
later of

- the Subcontract Date and
- the date when the *Contractor* receives the advanced payment bond.

The advanced payment bond is issued by a bank or insurer which the *Contra
tor* has accepted. A reason for not accepting the proposed bank or insurer
that its commercial position is not strong enough to carry the bond. The bo
is for the amount of the advanced payment which the *Subcontractor* has n
repaid and is in the form set out in the Subcontract Works Information. Del
in making the advanced payment is a compensation event.

X14.3 The advanced payment is repaid to the *Contractor* by the *Subcontractor*
instalments of the amount stated in the Subcontract Data. An instalment
included in each amount due assessed after the period stated in the Subco
tract Data has passed until the advanced payment has been repaid.

Option X15: Limitation of the *Subcontractor*'s liability for his design to reasonable skill and care

The *Subcontractor*'s design **X15**

X15.1 The *Subcontractor* is not liable for Defects in the *subcontract works* due to h
design so far as he proves that he used reasonable skill and care to ensu
that his design complied with the Subcontract Works Information.

X15.2 If the *Subcontractor* corrects a Defect for which he is not liable under th
subcontract it is a compensation event.

ption X16: Retention

Retention **X16**

X16.1 After the Price for Work Done to Date has reached the *retention free amount*, an amount is retained in each amount due. Until the earlier of

- Completion of the whole of the *subcontract works* and
- the date on which the *Contractor* takes over the whole of the *subcontract works*

the amount retained is the *retention percentage* applied to the excess of the Price for Work Done to Date above the *retention free amount*.

X16.2 The amount retained is halved

- in the assessment made at Completion of the whole of the *subcontract works* or
- in the next assessment after the *Contractor* has taken over the whole of the *subcontract works* if this is before Completion of the whole of the *subcontract works*.

The amount retained remains at this amount until the Defects Certificate is issued. No amount is retained in the assessments made after the Defects Certificate has been issued.

ption X17: Low performance damages

Low performance **X17**
damages X17.1 If a Defect included in the Defects Certificate shows low performance with respect to a performance level stated in the Subcontract Data, the *Subcontractor* pays the amount of low performance damages stated in the Subcontract Data.

ption X18: Limitation of liability

Limitation of liability **X18**

X18.1 The *Subcontractor*'s liability to the *Contractor* for the *Contractor*'s indirect or consequential loss is limited to the amount stated in the Subcontract Data.

X18.2 For any one event, the liability of the *Subcontractor* to the *Contractor* for loss of or damage to the *Employer*'s or *Contractor*'s property is limited to the amount stated in the Subcontract Data.

X18.3 The *Subcontractor*'s liability to the *Contractor* for Defects due to his design which are not listed on the Defects Certificate is limited to the amount stated in the Subcontract Data.

X18.4 The *Subcontractor*'s total liability to the *Contractor* for all matters arising under or in connection with this subcontract, other than the excluded matters, is limited to the amount stated in the Subcontract Data and applies in contract, tort or delict and otherwise to the extent allowed under the *law of the subcontract*.

The excluded matters are amounts payable by the *Subcontractor* as stated in this subcontract for

- loss of or damage to the *Employer*'s or the *Contractor*'s property,
- delay damages if Option X7 applies,
- low performance damages if Option X17 applies and
- *Subcontractor*'s share if Option C or Option D applies.

core
clauses

main
option clauses

secondary
option clauses

cost
components

subcontract
data

X18.5 The *Subcontractor* is not liable to the *Contractor* for a matter unless it notified to the *Subcontractor* before the *end of liability date*.

Option X20: Key Performance Indicators (not used with Option X12)

Incentives X20.1 A Key Performance Indicator is an aspect of performance by the *Subcontrac* for which a target is stated in the Incentive Schedule. The Incentive Schedule the *incentive schedule* unless later changed in accordance with this subcontra

X20.2 From the *subcontract starting date* until the Defects Certificate has be issued, the *Subcontractor* reports to the *Contractor* his performance agair each of the Key Performance Indicators. Reports are provided at the interva stated in the Subcontract Data and include the forecast final measureme against each indicator.

X20.3 If the *Subcontractor*'s forecast final measurement against a Key Performar Indicator will not achieve the target stated in the Incentive Schedule, submits to the *Contractor* his proposals for improving performance.

X20.4 The *Subcontractor* is paid the amount stated in the Incentive Schedule if t target stated for a Key Performance Indicator is improved upon or achieve Payment of the amount is due when the target has been improved upon achieved.

X20.5 The *Contractor* may add a Key Performance Indicator and associated payme to the Incentive Schedule but may not delete or reduce a payment stated the Incentive Schedule.

TION Y

tion Y(UK)2: The Housing Grants, Construction and Regeneration Act 1996

Definitions	**Y(UK)2**	
	Y2.1	(1) The Act is The Housing Grants, Construction and Regeneration Act 1996.
		(2) A period of time stated in days is a period calculated in accordance with Section 116 of the Act.
Dates for payment	Y2.2	The date on which a payment becomes due is seven days after the assessment date.
		The final date for payment is fourteen days or a different period for payment if stated in the Subcontract Data after the date on which payment becomes due.
		The *Contractor*'s certificate is the notice of payment from the *Contractor* to the *Subcontractor* specifying the amount of the payment made or proposed to be made and stating how the amount was calculated.
Notice of intention to withhold payment	Y2.3	If either Party intends to withhold payment of an amount due under this subcontract, he notifies the other Party not later than seven days (the prescribed period) before the final date for payment by stating the amount proposed to be withheld and the reason for withholding payment. If there is more than one reason, the amount for each reason is stated.
		A Party does not withhold payment of an amount due under this subcontract unless he has notified his intention to withhold payment as required by this subcontract.
Suspension of performance	Y2.4	If the *Subcontractor* exercises his right under the Act to suspend performance, it is a compensation event.

tion Y(UK)3: The Contracts (Rights of Third Parties) Act 1999

Third party rights	**Y(UK)3**	
	Y3.1	A person or organisation who is not one of the Parties may enforce a term of this subcontract under the Contracts (Rights of Third Parties) Act 1999 only if the term and the person or organisation are stated in the Subcontract Data.

tion Z: *Additional conditions of subcontract*

Additional conditions of subcontract	**Z1**	
	Z1.1	The *additional conditions of subcontract* stated in the Subcontract Data are part of this subcontract.

core clauses

main option clauses

secondary option clauses

cost components

subcontract data

SCHEDULE OF COST COMPONENTS

core clauses

main option clauses

secondary option clauses

cost components

subcontract data

This schedule is part of the *conditions of subcontract* only when Option C, E is used. In this schedule the *Subcontractor* means the *Subcontractor* not his Subsubcontractors. An amount is included only in one cost compor and only if it is incurred in order to Provide the Subcontract Works.

People 1 The following components of the cost of

- people who are directly employed by the *Subcontractor* and wh normal place of working is within the Working Areas and
- people who are directly employed by the *Subcontractor* and wh normal place of working is not within the Working Areas but who working in the Working Areas.

11 Wages, salaries and amounts paid by the *Subcontractor* for people according to the time worked while they are within the Working Areas.

12 Payments to people for

  (a) bonuses and incentives
  (b) overtime
  (c) working in special circumstances
  (d) special allowances
  (e) absence due to sickness and holidays
  (f) severance related to work on this subcontract.

13 Payments made in relation to people for

  (a) travel
  (b) subsistence and lodging
  (c) relocation
  (d) medical examinations
  (e) passports and visas
  (f) travel insurance
  (g) items (a) to (f) for dependants
  (h) protective clothing
  (i) meeting the requirements of the law
  (j) pensions and life assurance
  (k) death benefit
  (l) occupational accident benefits
  (m) medical aid
  (n) a vehicle
  (o) safety training.

14 The following components of the cost of people who are not directly emplc by the *Subcontractor* but are paid for by him according to the time wor while they are within the Working Areas.

  Amounts paid by the *Subcontractor*.

Equipment 2 The following components of the cost of Equipment which is used within Working Areas (including the cost of accommodation but excluding Equipn cost covered by the percentage for Working Areas overheads).

21 Payments for the hire or rent of Equipment not owned by

- the *Subcontractor*,
- his parent company or
- by a company with the same parent company

at the hire or rental rate multiplied by the time for which the Equipmer required.

22   Payments for Equipment which is not listed in the Subcontract Data but is

- owned by the *Subcontractor*,
- purchased by the *Subcontractor* under a hire purchase or lease agreement or
- hired by the *Subcontractor* from the *Subcontractor*'s parent company or another part of a group with the same parent company

at open market rates multiplied by the time for which the Equipment is required.

23   Payments for Equipment purchased for work included in this subcontract listed with a time-related on cost charge, in the Subcontract Data, of

- the change in value over the period for which the Equipment is required and
- the time-related on cost charge stated in the Subcontract Data for the period for which the Equipment is required.

The change in value is the difference between the purchase price and either the sale price or the open market sale price at the end of the period for which the Equipment is required. Interim payments of the change in value are made at each assessment date. A final payment is made in the next assessment after the change in value has been determined.

If the *Contractor* agrees, an additional item of Equipment may be assessed as if it had been listed in the Subcontract Data.

24   Payments for special Equipment that is listed in the Subcontract Data. These amounts are the rates stated in the Subcontract Data multiplied by the time for which the Equipment is required.

If the *Contractor* agrees, an additional item of special Equipment may be assessed as if it had been listed in the Subcontract Data.

25   Payments for the purchase price of Equipment which is consumed.

26   Unless included in the hire or rental rates, payments for

- transporting Equipment to and from the Working Areas other than for repair and maintenance
- erecting and dismantling Equipment and
- constructing, fabricating or modifying Equipment as a result of a compensation event.

27   Payments for purchase of materials used to construct or fabricate Equipment.

28   Unless included in the hire rates, the cost of operatives is included in the cost of people.

Plant and Materials 3   The following components of the cost of Plant and Materials.

31   Payments for

- purchasing Plant and Materials,
- delivery to and removal from the Working Areas,
- providing and removing packaging and
- samples and tests.

32   Cost is credited with payments received for disposal of Plant and Materials unless the cost is disallowed.

Charges 4   The following components of the cost of charges paid by the *Subcontractor*.

41   Payments for provision and use in the Working Areas of

- water,
- gas and
- electricity.

   55

core clauses

main option clauses

secondary option clauses

cost components

subcontract data

42 Payments to public authorities and other properly constituted authorities charges which they are authorised to make in respect of the *subcontr* *works*.

43 Payments for

(a) cancellation charges arising from a compensation event
(b) buying or leasing land
(c) compensation for loss of crops or buildings
(d) royalties
(e) inspection certificates
(f) charges for access to the Working Areas
(g) facilities for visits to the Working Areas by Others
(h) specialist services
(i) consumables and equipment provided by the *Subcontractor* for the *Contractor*'s office.

44 A charge for overhead costs incurred within the Working Areas calculated applying the percentage for Working Areas overheads stated in the Subc tract Data to the total of people items 11, 12, 13 and 14. The cha includes provision and use of equipment, supplies and services, but exclu accommodation, for

(a) catering
(b) medical facilities and first aid
(c) recreation
(d) sanitation
(e) security
(f) copying
(g) telephone, telex, fax, radio and CCTV
(h) surveying and setting out
(i) computing
(j) hand tools not powered by compressed air.

Manufacture and fabrication 5 The following components of the cost of manufacture and fabrication of Pl and Materials which are

• wholly or partly designed specifically for the *subcontract works* and
• manufactured or fabricated outside the Working Areas.

51 The total of the hours worked by employees multiplied by the hourly ra stated in the Subcontract Data for the categories of employees listed.

52 An amount for overheads calculated by multiplying this total by the perc tage for manufacturing and fabrication overheads stated in the Subcontr Data.

Design 6 The following components of the cost of design of the *subcontract works* a Equipment done outside the Working Areas.

61 The total of the hours worked by employees multiplied by the hourly ra stated in the Subcontract Data for the categories of employees listed.

62 An amount for overheads calculated by multiplying this total by the perc tage for design overheads stated in the Subcontract Data.

63 The cost of travel to and from the Working Areas for the categories of des employees listed in the Subcontract Data.

Insurance 7 The following are deducted from cost

• the cost of events for which this subcontract requires the *Subcontrac* to insure and
• other costs paid to the *Subcontractor* by insurers.

SHORTER SCHEDULE OF COST COMPONENTS

This schedule is part of the *conditions of subcontract* only when Option A, B, C, D or E is used. When Option C, D or E is used, this schedule is used by agreement for assessing compensation events. When Option C, D or E is used, in this schedule the *Subcontractor* means the *Subcontractor* and not his Subsubcontractors. An amount is included only in one cost component and only if it is incurred in order to Provide the Subcontract Works.

People 1 The following components of the cost of

- people who are directly employed by the *Subcontractor* and whose normal place of working is within the Working Areas,
- people who are directly employed by the *Subcontractor* and whose normal place of working is not within the Working Areas but who are working in the Working Areas and
- people who are not directly employed by the *Subcontractor* but are paid for by him according to the time worked while they are within the Working Areas.

11 Amounts paid by the *Subcontractor* including those for meeting the requirements of the law and for pension provision.

Equipment 2 The following components of the cost of Equipment which is used within the Working Areas (including the cost of accommodation but excluding Equipment cost covered by the percentage for people overheads).

21 Amounts for Equipment which is in the published list stated in the Subcontract Data. These amounts are calculated by applying the percentage adjustment for listed Equipment stated in the Subcontract Data to the rates in the published list and by multiplying the resulting rate by the time for which the Equipment is required.

22 Amounts for Equipment listed in the Subcontract Data which is not in the published list stated in the Subcontract Data. These amounts are the rates stated in the Subcontract Data multiplied by the time for which the Equipment is required.

23 The time required is expressed in hours, days, weeks or months consistently with the list of items of Equipment in the Subcontract Data or with the published list stated in the Subcontract Data.

24 Unless the item is in the published list and the rate includes the cost component, payments for

- transporting Equipment to and from the Working Areas other than for repair and maintenance,
- erecting and dismantling Equipment and
- constructing, fabricating or modifying Equipment as a result of a compensation event.

25 Unless the item is in the published list and the rate includes the cost component, the purchase price of Equipment which is consumed.

26 Unless included in the rate in the published list, the cost of operatives is included in the cost of people.

core clauses

main option clauses

secondary option clauses

cost components

subcontract data

core
clauses

main
option clauses

secondary
option clauses

cost
components

subcontract
data

27   Amounts for Equipment which is neither in the published list, stated in Subcontract Data nor listed in the Subcontract Data, at competitively tende or open market rates, multiplied by the time for which the Equipment required.

Plant and Materials   **3**   The following components of the cost of Plant and Materials.

31   Payments for

- purchasing Plant and Materials,
- delivery to and removal from the Working Areas,
- providing and removing packaging and
- samples and tests.

32   Cost is credited with payments received for disposal of Plant and Materi unless the cost is disallowed.

Charges   **4**

41   The following components of the cost of charges paid by the *Subcontractor.*

A charge calculated by applying the percentage for people overheads sta in the Subcontract Data to people item 11 to cover the costs of

- payments for the provision and use in the Working Areas of water, g and electricity,
- payments for buying or leasing land, compensation for loss of crops buildings, royalties, inspection certificates, charges for access to ' Working Areas and facilities for visits to the Working Areas by Others a
- payments for equipment, supplies and services for offices, drawing offi laboratories, workshops, stores and compounds, labour camps, cabi catering, medical facilities and first aid, recreation, sanitation, secur copying, telephone, telex, fax, radio, CCTV, surveying and setting c computing, and hand tools not powered by compressed air.

42   Payments for cancellation charges arising from a compensation event.

43   Payments to public authorities and other properly constituted authorities charges which they are authorised to make in respect of the *subcontr works.*

44   Consumables and equipment provided by the *Subcontractor* for the *Contr tor*'s office.

45   Specialist services.

Manufacture and   **5**   The following components of the cost of manufacture and fabrication of Pl
fabrication   and Materials, which are

- wholly or partly designed specifically for the *subcontract works* and
- manufactured or fabricated outside the Working Areas.

51   Amounts paid by the *Subcontractor.*

Design   **6**   The following components of the cost of design of the *subcontract works* a Equipment done outside the Working Areas.

61   The total of the hours worked by employees multiplied by the hourly ra stated in the Subcontract Data for the categories of employees listed.

62   An amount for overheads calculated by multiplying this total by the perc tage for design overheads stated in the Subcontract Data.

63   The cost of travel to and from the Working Areas for the categories of des employees listed in the Subcontract Data.

Insurance   **7**   The following are deducted from cost:

- costs against which this subcontract required the *Subcontractor* to ins and
- other costs paid to the *Subcontractor* by insurers.

rt one – Data provided by the *Contractor*

Completion of the data in full, according to the Options chosen, is essential to create a complete subcontract.

Statements given in all subcontracts

1 General

- The *conditions of contract* are the core clauses and the clauses for main Option ....., dispute resolution Option ..... and secondary Options ..... of the NEC3 Engineering and Construction Subcontract (June 2005).

- The *works* in the main contract are

  ....

- The *subcontract works* are

  ....

- The *Contractor* is

  Name ....

  Address ....

  ....

- The *Employer* in the main contract is

  Name ....

  Address ....

  ....

- The *Project Manager* in the main contract is

  Name ....

  Address ....

  ....

- The *Supervisor* in the main contract is

  Name ....

  Address ....

  ....

- The *Adjudicator* in this subcontract is

  Name ....

  Address ....

  ....

(side tabs: core clauses | main option clauses | secondary option clauses | cost components | subcontract data)

- The *main contract Adjudicator* is

  Name . . . .

  Address . . . .

  . . . .

- The Subcontract Works Information is in

  . . . .

  . . . .

  . . . .

- The Site Information is in

  . . . .

  . . . .

  . . . .

- The *boundaries of the site* are. . . . .

- The *language of this subcontract* is. . . . .

- The *law of the subcontract* is the law of . . . .

- The *period for reply* is

  for a reply by the *Contractor* . . . . wee

  for a reply by the *Subcontractor* . . . . wee

- The *Adjudicator nominating body* is. . . . .

- The *tribunal* is . . . .

  . . . .

- The following matters will be included in the Risk Register

  . . . .

  . . . .

  . . . .

3 Time

- The *subcontract starting date* is . . . .

- The *subcontract access dates* are

Part of the Site	Date
1	. . . .
2	. . . .
3	. . . .

- The *Subcontractor* submits revised programmes at intervals no longer th

  . . . . wee

4 Testing and Defects

- The *defects date* is . . . . weeks after Completion of the whole the *subcontract works*.

- The *defect correction period* is . . . . weeks except t

  - The *defect correction period* for . . . . is . . . . wee

  - The *defect correction period* for . . . . is . . . . wee

5 Payment

- The *currency of this subcontract* is the . . . .
- The *assessment interval* is . . . . weeks (not more than five).
- The *interest rate* is . . . .% per annum (not less than 2) above the . . . .

  rate of the . . . . bank.

6 Compensation events

- The place where weather is to be recorded is

  . . . .

- The *weather measurements* to be recorded for each calendar month are

  - the cumulative rainfall (mm)
  - the number of days with rainfall more than 5 mm
  - the number of days with minimum air temperature less than 0 degrees Celsius
  - the number of days with snow lying at . . . . hours GMT
  - and these measurements:

    . . . .

    . . . .

    . . . .

- The *weather measurements* are supplied by . . . .
- The *weather data* are the records of past *weather measurements* for each

  calendar month which were recorded at . . . .

  and which are available from . . . .

  . . . .

Where no recorded data are available

- Assumed values for the ten year return *weather data* for each *weather measurement* for each calendar month are

  . . . .

  . . . .

  . . . .

  . . . .

8 Risks and insurance

- The minimum limit of indemnity for insurance in respect of loss of or damage to property (except the *subcontract works*, Plant and Materials and Equipment) and liability for bodily injury to or death of a person (not an employee of the *Subcontractor*) caused by activity in connection with this subcontract for any one event is

  . . . .

- The minimum limit of indemnity for insurance in respect of death of or bodily injury to employees of the *Subcontractor* arising out of and in the course of their employment in connection with this subcontract for any one event is

  . . . .

core clauses

main option clauses

secondary option clauses

cost components

subcontract data

Optional statements

If the *tribunal* is arbitration

- The *arbitration procedure* is . . . .

- The place where the arbitration is to be held is

  . . . .

- The person or organisation who will choose an arbitrator

  - if the Parties cannot agree a choice or

  - if the *arbitration procedure* does not state who selects an arbitrator is

  . . . .

If the *Contractor* has decided the *subcontract completion date* for the whole the *subcontract works*

- The *subcontract completion date* for the whole of the *subcontract works* is

  . . . .

If the *Contractor* is not willing to take over the *subcontract works* before Subcontract Completion Date

- The *Contractor* is not willing to take over the *subcontract works* before Subcontract Completion Date.

If no programme is identified in part two of the Subcontract Data

- The *Subcontractor* is to submit a first programme for acceptance with

  . . . . weeks of the Subcontract Da

If the *Contractor* has identified work which is to meet a stated *condition* b *key date*

- The *key dates* and *conditions* to be met are

condition to be met	*key date*
1	. . . .
2	. . . .
3	. . . .

If the period in which payments are made is not four weeks and Y(UK)2 is used

- The period within which payments are made is . . . .

If Y(UK)2 is used and the final date for payment is not 21 days after the d when payment is due

- The period for payment is . . . .

If there are additional compensation events

- These are additional compensation events

  1 . . . .

  2 . . . .

  3 . . . .

core clauses

main option clauses

secondary option clauses

cost components

subcontract data

If there are additional *Employer*'s or *Contractor*'s risks

- These are additional *Employer*'s risks

    1 . . . .

    2 . . . .

    3 . . . .

- These are additional *Contractor*'s risks

    1 . . . .

    2 . . . .

    3 . . . .

If the *Employer* or *Contractor* is to provide Plant and Materials

- The insurance against loss of or damage to the *subcontract works*, Plant and Materials is to include cover for Plant and Materials provided by the *Employer* or *Contractor* for an amount of

    . . . .

If the *Employer* or *Contractor* is to provide any of the insurances stated in the Insurance Table

- The *Employer* or *Contractor* provides these insurances from the Insurance Table

    1. Insurance against. . . . .

    Cover/indemnity is . . . .

    The deductibles are. . . . .

    2. Insurance against. . . . .

    Cover/indemnity is . . . .

    The deductibles are. . . . .

    3. Insurance against. . . . .

    Cover/indemnity is . . . .

    The deductibles are. . . . .

If additional insurances are to be provided

- The *Employer* or *Contractor* provides these additional insurances

    1. Insurance against. . . . .

    Cover/indemnity is . . . .

    The deductibles are. . . . .

    2. Insurance against. . . . .

    Cover/indemnity is . . . .

    The deductibles are. . . . .

    3. Insurance against. . . . .

    Cover/indemnity is . . . .

    The deductibles are. . . . .

- The *Subcontractor* provides these additional insurances
  1. Insurance against . . . .
  Cover/indemnity is . . . .
  2. Insurance against . . . .
  Cover/indemnity is . . . .
  3. Insurance against . . . .
  Cover/indemnity is . . . .

If Option B or D is used

- The *method of measurement* is . . . .
  amended as follows . . . .
  . . . .
  . . . .

If Option C or D is used

- The *Subcontractor's share percentages* and the *share ranges* are

share range	Subcontractor's share percentage
less than . . . . %	. . . .
from . . . . % to . . . . %	. . . .
from . . . . % to . . . . %	. . . .
greater than . . . . %	. . . .

If Option C, D or E is used

- The *Subcontractor* prepares forecasts of Defined Cost for the *subcontr*
  works at intervals no longer than . . . . wee
- The *exchange rates* are those published in . . . .
  on . . . . (dat

If Option X1 is used

- The proportions used to calculate the Price Adjustment Factor are
  0 . . . . linked to the index for . . . .
  0 . . . .
  0 . . . .
  0 . . . .
  0 . . . .
  0 . . . .
  0 . . . . non-adjustable
  _____
  1.00
- The *base date* for indices is . . . .
- The indices are those prepared by . . . .

---

core clauses

main option clauses

secondary option clauses

cost components

subcontract data

If Option X3 is used

- The *Contractor* will pay for the items or activities listed below in the currencies stated

items and activities	other currency	total maximum payment in the currency
. . . .	. . . .	. . . .
. . . .	. . . .	. . . .
. . . .	. . . .	. . . .
. . . .	. . . .	. . . .

- The *exchange rates* are those published in . . . .

  on . . . . (date).

If Option X5 is used

- The *subcontract completion date* for each *section* of the *subcontract works* is

section	description	*subcontract completion date*
1	. . . .	. . . .
2	. . . .	. . . .
3	. . . .	. . . .
4	. . . .	. . . .

If Options X5 and X6 are used together

- The bonus for each *section* of the *subcontract works* is

section	description	amount per day
1	. . . .	. . . .
2	. . . .	. . . .
3	. . . .	. . . .
4	. . . .	. . . .

  Remainder of the *subcontract works* . . . .

If Options X5 and X7 are used together

- Delay damages for each *section* of the *subcontract works* are

section	description	amount per day
1	. . . .	. . . .
2	. . . .	. . . .
3	. . . .	. . . .
4	. . . .	. . . .

  Remainder of the *subcontract works* . . . .

If Option X6 is used (but not if Option X5 is also used)

- The bonus for the whole of the *subcontract works* is . . . . per day.

core clauses

main option clauses

secondary option clauses

cost components

subcontract data

If Option X7 is used (but not if Option X5 is also used)

- Delay damages for Completion of the whole of the *subcontract works*
  . . . . per day.

If Option X12 is used

- The *Client* is

  Name . . . .

  Address . . . .

  . . . .

- The *Client's objective* is

  . . . .

  . . . .

  . . . .

  . . . .

  . . . .

  . . . .

- The Partnering Information is in

  . . . .

  . . . .

  . . . .

  . . . .

If Option X13 is used

- The amount of the performance bond is . . . .

If Option X14 is used

- The amount of the advanced payment is . . . .
- The *Subcontractor* repays the instalments in assessments starting not le

  than . . . . weeks after the Subcontract Da

- The instalments are. . . . .

  . . . .

  (either an amount or a percentage of the payment otherwise due)

- An advanced payment bond <u>is/is not</u> required.

If Option X16 is used

- The *retention free amount* is. . . . .
- The *retention percentage* is . . . .

If Option X17 is used

- The amounts for low performance damages are

amount	performance level
. . . .	for . . . .
. . . .	for . . . .
. . . .	for . . . .
. . . .	for . . . .

core clauses

main option clauses

secondary option clauses

cost components

subcontract data

If Option X18 is used

- The *Subcontractor*'s liability to the *Contractor* for indirect or consequential loss is limited to . . . .

- For any one event, the *Subcontractor*'s liability to the *Contractor* for loss of or damage to the *Employer*'s or *Contractor*'s property is limited to . . . .

- The *Subcontractor*'s liability for Defects due to his design which are not listed on the Defects Certificate is limited to . . . .

- The *Subcontractor*'s total liability to the *Contractor* for all matters arising under or in connection with this subcontract, other than the excluded matters, is limited to . . . .

- The *end of liability date* is . . . . years after the Completion of the whole of the *subcontract works*.

If Option X20 is used (but not if Option X12 is also used)

- The *incentive schedule* for Key Performance Indicators is in . . . .

- A report of performance against each Key Performance Indicator is provided at intervals of . . . . months.

If Option Y(UK)3 is used

- term   person or organisation

  . . . .

  . . . .

  . . . .

  . . . .

If Option Z is used

- The *additional conditions of subcontract* are . . . .

  . . . .

core clauses

main option clauses

secondary option clauses

cost components

subcontract data

Part two – Data provided by the *Subcontractor*

Completion of the data in full, according to the Options chosen, is essent
to create a complete subcontract.

Statements given in all subcontracts

- The *Subcontractor* is

  Name . . . .

  Address . . . .

  . . . .

- The *direct fee percentage* is . . . .

- The *subsubcontracted fee percentage* is. . . . .

- The *subcontract working areas* are the Site and . . . .

- The key people are

  (1) Name. . . . .

  Job . . . .

  Responsibilities. . . . .

  . . . .

  Qualifications . . . .

  Experience. . . . .

  . . . .

  (2) Name. . . . .

  Job . . . .

  Responsibilities. . . . .

  . . . .

  Qualifications. . . . .

  Experience. . . . .

  . . . .

- The following matters will be included in the Risk Register

  . . . .

  . . . .

  . . . .

  . . . .

Optional statements

If the *Subcontractor* is to provide Subcontract Works Information for his design

- The Subcontract Works Information for the *Subcontractor*'s design is in

....

....

....

....

....

....

If a programme is to be identified in the Subcontract Data

- The programme identified in the Subcontract Data is ....

If the *Subcontractor* is to decide the *completion date* for the whole of the *subcontract works*

- The *subcontract completion date* for the whole of the *subcontract works* is ....

If Option A or C is used

- The *activity schedule* is ....

If Option B or D is used

- The *bill of quantities* is...

If Option A, B, C or D is used

- The tendered total of the Prices is ....

If Option A or B is used

Data for the Shorter Schedule of Cost Components

- The percentage for people overheads is...........................%.
- The published list of Equipment is the last edition of the list published by ....
- The percentage for adjustment for Equipment in the published list is .... % (state plus or minus).
- The rates for other Equipment are

Equipment	size or capacity	rate
....	....	....
....	....	....
....	....	....
....	....	....

- The hourly rates for Defined Cost of design outside the Working Areas are

category of employee	hourly rate
....	....
....	....
....	....
....	....

Side tabs: core clauses | main option clauses | secondary option clauses | cost components | **subcontract data**

- The percentage for design overheads is. . . . .%.
- The categories of design employees whose travelling expenses to and from the Working Areas are included in Defined Cost are

. . . .

. . . .

. . . .

. . . .

If Option C, D or E is used

Data for Schedule of Cost Components

- The listed items of Equipment purchased for work on this subcontract, with an on cost charge, are

Equipment	time-related charge	per time period
. . . .	. . . .	per . . . .
. . . .	. . . .	per . . . .
. . . .	. . . .	per . . . .
. . . .	. . . .	per . . . .

- The rates for special Equipment are

Equipment	size or capacity	rate
. . . .	. . . .	. . . .
. . . .	. . . .	. . . .
. . . .	. . . .	. . . .
. . . .	. . . .	. . . .

- The percentage for Working Areas overheads is . . . .%.
- The hourly rates for Defined Cost of manufacture and fabrication outside the Working Areas are

category of employee	hourly rate
. . . .	. . . .
. . . .	. . . .
. . . .	. . . .
. . . .	. . . .

- The percentage for manufacture and fabrication overheads is . . . .%.

If Option C, D or E is used

Data for both schedules of cost components

- The hourly rates for Defined Cost of design outside the Working Areas are

category of employee	hourly rate
. . . .	. . . .
. . . .	. . . .
. . . .	. . . .
. . . .	. . . .

- The percentage for design overheads is. . . . .%

- The categories of design employees whose travelling expenses to and from the Working Areas are included as a cost of design of the *subcontract works* and Equipment done outside of the Working Areas are

....

....

....

....

If Option C, D or E is used

Data for the Shorter Schedule of Cost Components

- The percentage for people overheads is..........................%.
- The published list of Equipment is the last edition of the list published by

....

- The percentage for adjustment for Equipment in the published list is

.... % (state plus or minus).

- The rates for other Equipment are

Equipment	size or capacity	rate
....	....	....
....	....	....
....	....	....
....	....	....

core clauses

main option clauses

secondary option clauses

cost components

subcontract data

© copyright nec 2005

nec 3 Engineering and Construction Subcontract

Index by clause numbers (Option clauses are indicated by their letters, main clause heads by bold numbers).
Terms in *italics* are identified in Subcontract Data, and defined terms have capital initial letters.

demolition 22.1, 73.2
design
Contractor's 80.1
Employer's 80.1
Subcontract Equipment **23**
subcontract works C20.3, D20.3, E20.3
Subcontractor's 11.2(5), 21.2, 21.3, 22.1, 23.1, 27.1
direct fee percentage 11.2(8), 93.2
Disallowed Cost C11.2(23), D11.2(23), E11.2(23)
definition(s) C11.2(25), D11.2(25), E11.2(25)
discounts, deduction from prices 52.1
dismantling (during searching) 42.1
dispute resolution
unless United Kingdom Housing Grants, Construction and Regeneration Act (1996) applies **W1**
when United Kingdom Housing Grants, Construction and Regeneration Act (1996) applies **W2**

early Completion bonus X6.1
early warning **16**
effects 16.1, 32.1
responsibility 16.1, 61.5, 63.5, C11.2(25), D11.2(25), E11.2(25)
Risk Register 11.2(14)
employees
Adjudicator's W1.2(5), W2.2(5)
Subcontractor's 24.1, 24.2, 84.2
Employer
Defects Certificate 43.3
fault 80.1
hindered by Subcontractor 91.3
indemnity 83.1
insurance 84.1, **87**
programme 31.2, 60.1(5)
responsibilities 87.2
risks 60.1(14), **80**, 81.1, 83.2, 85.4
Subcontract Works Information 60.1(5)
tests and inspections 40.2, 60.1(16)
use of subcontract works 11.2(2), 35.2
Employer's design 80.1
Equipment
damage to 80.1, 84.2
definition 11.2(7)
design of **23**
left on Site 72.1, 80.1
loss of 80.1, 84.2
marking of 71.1
and programme 31.2
rates in Subcontract Data X1.3
removal of **72**, 92.2, 93.2
title 92.2
use by Contractor 92.2
errors, Adjudicator W1.3(11)
excavation materials 73.2
exchange rates C50.6, D50.6, E50.7, X3.1
experienced contractor
and compensation events 60.1(12), 60.2, 61.5, 63.5
and physical conditions on Site 60.1(12), 60.2
extension of time for decision/quotation/reply 13.5, 62.5

facilities and services, for tests/inspections 40.2, 42.1, 60.1(16)
failure to pay in time, actions to be taken 91.4
fault of
Contractor or his design 80.1
Employer or his design 80.1
Subcontractor 61.1, 61.4
Fee C11.2(29), D11.2(29), E11.2(29)(32)
calculation(s) 11.2(8), 63.1, 93.2, C50.6, D50.6, E50.7
Defined Cost 52.1
fee percentage see direct fee percentage
final decision, Adjudicator W1.3(10), W2.3(11)
float, provision in programme 31.2
forecasts 61.6, 63.1, 65.2, 93.2, C20.4, C53.3, D20.4, D53.7, E20.4, E65.3
fraud, and insurance 85.2

grouping of activities A11.2(27), A93.3
guarantee(s) 91.2, X4.1

health and safety
regulation(s) 91.3
requirements 31.2
Subcontract Works Information 27.4
Subcontractor 27.4
historical-interest objects found within Site 60.1(7), 73.1
Housing Grants, Construction and Regeneration Act (1996) **W1**, **W2**, **Y(UK)2**

identified terms **11**
illegal requirements **18**
implementing compensation events 32.1, **65**, A65.4, B65.4, C65.4, D65.4, E65.3
impossible requirements **18**
incentive schedule X20.1
Incentive Schedule X20.1, X20.3–5
inconsistencies **17**, 60.3, 63.8, B60.6–7, D60.6–7
indemnity **83**
information
in Activity Schedule A54.1, C54.1
in Bill of Quantities B55.1, D55.1
later recorded 65.2
in programme 31.2, 31.3, 50.3
provided to Others 25.1
publicly available 60.2
see also Site Information; Subcontract Works Information
injury insurance 84.2
inspection(s) **40**, 60.1(10)(11)
before delivery **41**
costs for repeats E40.7
instalment repayment of advanced payment X14.3
instruction(s)
Adjudicator's W2.3(4–5)
compensation events resulting 60.1(1)(4)(7), 61.1
to Contractor 27.3
form of communication 13.1
insurance 87.1
objects of value/interest 60.1(7)